How could she ever have imagined he might have changed in his attitude towards her? Any softening of his feelings towards her was merely temporary, born of the danger from which he had resued her.

'I can manage.'

Before she could protest further he bent towards her and started rubbing her wet hair with the towel. It was a vigorous action and yet in some odd way she was enjoying it. And she knew that this wasn't the effect of chill and exhaustion. His nearness was doing things to her, chasing away the feeling of exhaustion and bringing in its place a wild sweet happiness.

She struggled to wrench herself back to some sort of sanity. This was Craig, whom she hated more than any man she had ever met in her life. Remember?

PACIFIC PARADISE

BY

GLORIA BEVAN

MILLS & BOON LIMITED
ETON HOUSE   18-24 PARADISE ROAD
RICHMOND   SURREY   TW9 1SR

*First published in Great Britain 1989
by Mills & Boon Limited*

© Gloria Bevan 1989

*Australian copyright 1989
Philippine copyright 1989
This edition 1989*

ISBN 0 263 76242 4

*Set in Plantin 11 on 11 pt.
01 – 8903 – 58403*

Typeset in Great Britain by JCL Graphics, Bristol

Made and printed in Great Britain

CHAPTER ONE

JUST at first Joanne was scarcely aware of the man already seated in the cabin of the Air New Zealand plane waiting on the tarmac, a plane soon to take off on its long haul over the dark waters of the South Pacific ocean on its way to the tiny speck of land that was the island of Rarotonga.

It's happening! It's really happening at last! Joanne exulted as she slipped into her seat. In a few hours' time I'll be meeting Rick! We'll be together again—at last.

Rapt in her imaginings, she was in no mood to notice anything or anyone. Or so she thought until a resonant masculine voice cut across her musing. 'Care for the window seat?'

She slanted a glance towards the stranger at her side, to be immediately charmed by the man with the heart-knocking smile. She had a swift impression of a strong sun-tanned face, of smile-lines running down on either side of firmly set lips. The thought raced through her mind that he was devastatingly attractive. And yet there was something . . . a hint of steel in the unnerving pale blue eyes, eyes from which she seemed unable to avert her gaze.

At last she wrenched her glance aside. 'Thanks, but I'm OK.' She smiled a greeting. Somehow tonight she felt like smiling at everyone. For heaven's sake girl, she chided herself the next minute, it's time you kept that appointment on the island with Rick. High time when a perfect stranger can affect you this way, even if he does happen to be very attractive.

She concentrated her attention on a group of late arrivals. A number of young men, members of a sporting team judging by their matching blazers, were making their way down the centre aisle of the cabin in search of seat numbers.

The team responded with interest to her scrutiny. To a man they threw warmly appreciative glances in the direction of the small, spunky-looking girl with a cloud of dark curls falling to her shoulders and startling blue eyes that radiated an air of suppressed excitement. Joanne, however, was accustomed to attracting such glances from admiring young males and took little notice.

Presently seat-belts were fastened, jet engines roared to life and soon the plane lifted from the lighted tarmac to soar upwards into a star-strewn sky.

All at once Joanne was feeling uncomfortably warm in the heat of the cabin. She tugged at the black velvet jacket that had been her constant stand-by throughout the mild New Zealand winter she was fast leaving behind her.

'Let me help you!' Her neighbour, who had been intent on studying what appeared to Joanne to be a sheet of architectural drawings outspread on his knee, leaned towards her. With a deft movement of a well-shaped hand he loosened the clinging garment from her shoulders. As he got to his feet to place the jacket on the rack overhead she took in the lithe grace of his hard-muscled body. She hadn't realised how tall he was.

'You sure won't be needing this where you're going!' He smiled down at her and she caught the flash of strong white teeth in a sun-bronzed face.

'I know! I know!' Excitement sparked lights in her blue eyes. 'Not that I've ever been to the island, and I can only afford to stay for a week—oh, my goodness!' Her hand flew to her mouth and her eyes were anxious. 'I thought I'd budgeted for this trip so carefully, and I forgot all about tipping at the hotel!'

'You can keep right on forgetting.' His lazy tones were reassuring. 'It doesn't go down on Rarotonga, offends the locals, actually. They have the quaint notion that if someone gives them something they're duty-bound to return the gift. And since they've never set eyes on you before they have no intention of giving you a present, can't understand why they should.'

Joanne let out a sigh of relief. 'Thank heaven for that!'

He grinned. 'If you want to give the islanders something, just smile. They always do!'

Her warm smile flashed out and all at once his glance sharpened with male interest. 'That's the way!'

The next moment she wondered if she had merely imagined the flicker of approval in his eyes.

'It's going to be a long night,' he was saying, 'we may as well get to know each other. Craig's the name. And you're——?'

'Joanne.'

'Joanne.' It was funny, she mused, but the way in which he said her perfectly ordinary name made it sound quite different. It was his voice that charmed her, she decided. Resonant and musical almost, one could call it caressing—that was, of course, if a girl happened to be in love with him. But not this girl! He held no romantic interest for her. How could he, when she was on her way to meet her own true love?

'You'll like Rarotonga.' His pleasant tones cut across her thoughts. 'It's a sort of Pacific paradise, and the

Cook Island folk are terrific. Outgoing, fun-loving, talented. Just wait until you see their dancing! It's brilliant! They have a knack of making everyone feel at home, part of the family.' All at once he seemed to be speaking his thoughts aloud. 'The relaxed way of life over there really gets you after a while. It did me!'

It came to her that he too had about him an air of excitement. Could it be, she wondered, that he was meeting a girl he loved on the island? She thrust the idle speculation aside. As if his love life mattered to her!

'A holiday, is it?' The masculine tones broke into her thoughts. 'You're cutting loose from the workaday world to grab yourself a week or so of sunshine with nothing on your mind but snorkelling and sunbathing?'

Joanne hesitated. 'I guess,' she admitted slowly, 'you could call it a holiday.'

'I get it.' Even without glancing towards him she was disconcertingly aware of the unnerving scrutiny of cool blue eyes. 'Boyfriend waiting for you over on the island?'

She flashed him a surprised glance. 'How did you guess?'

He laughed, an attractive chuckle deep in his throat. 'You look over the moon with excitement.'

'And it shows! I just can't help it.' Her soft lips quirked at the corners and her eyes were dreamy. 'It's something to be thrilled about, this trip. It is for me.' She just had to confide in someone. The words fell eagerly from her lips. 'Rick and I haven't seen each other for two years, would you believe?'

He raised an enquiring dark eyebrow. 'How come? How any guy could let——'

'Oh, it wasn't the way you think!' She cut across his

cool, amused tones. 'We were both of the same mind about the separation, at least——' Hurriedly she swept on. 'Rick's his name, Rick Mason. You may have heard of him. He's ever so well known among the yachting crowd in Auckland where I live.'

He shook his head, his magnetic eyes regarding her intently. 'He took a bit of persuading to part with you?' His low tones were tinged with amusement. 'Was that it?'

'Yes—no—that is——' She felt her voice lurching. Why was she babbling on like this? She drew a deep breath. 'Well, just at first, maybe.' Swiftly she ran on. 'But he didn't really mind. It suited him just fine, the two years' separation. You see, yachting happens to be his whole life——' She was aware of the quizzical expression in his eyes. 'Well, just about,' she amended.

All at once for no reason at all she could feel the pink creeping up her cheeks. It must surely be due to the heat of the cabin. Or could it be that she sensed this stranger had a disconcerting way of seeing through any pretence? But she wasn't telling him anything that wasn't the truth. Was she? She thrust away the disturbing thoughts, putting up a hand to push the dark tresses back from her forehead. 'Anyway, Rick had this dream. He'd crewed for yacht races over the years, the big ones. The Auckland-Suva race, the Whitbread Round the World Race, you know?' Something about his ironical gaze was making her feel uneasy. She heard her own voice babbling on. 'No wonder they call Auckland the "City of Sails".' Maybe if she avoided looking directly into his eyes she would rid herself of this stupid confusion. It helped, definitely. For now her tone was light and casual. A girl chatting inconsequentially to a fellow passenger on a long night flight. 'You see, what he planned was to build himself an ocean-going craft and sail around the islands of the South Pacific.'

'Some dream.'

'He thought so. He built his yacht too, right there in the backyard of the house he shared with three other yachting guys. He worked just about every spare minute, weekends, nights, any time he could get free from his work.' She heard her own voice running excitedly on. 'He was wrapped in his plans for his island cruise. The other guys at the house helped him with the building but he did most of the work himself. Luckily he happens to be a sailmaker by trade. Anyway, he got the boat finished at last, just two years ago. He named it——'

'Don't tell me,' came the lazy resonant tones. 'Would it be the *Joanne?*'

She had been prepared for that one. 'You've got it.'

After a moment she ran on. 'He planned to spend about two years drifting around the different islands, calling in at ports, getting to know the natives, their culture, life-style, you know?'

All at once the lightness died out of her voice and she twisted a strand of curly hair round and round her fingers in a nervous gesture. 'Actually, he wanted me to go with him on his island cruise.'

The lazy tones seemed scarcely interested. 'Why didn't you? What was the problem? Seasickness?'

'Crikey, no!' She gave a trill of laughter. She didn't know, for no one had ever told her, that her laugh, light and sweet and radiating happiness, was unforgettable. 'It was just something else that came up for me at the same time, something I'd wanted to do for ages.'

'More important to you than anything else in the world? Or anyone?' Did she imagine a note of mockery in the cool tones?

'Yes, it was!' she said with spirit. 'You see, being a schoolteacher, I had a chance of getting accepted for Voluntary Service Overseas. It was something I'd wanted to do for ever so long. When I got the letter telling me I'd been accepted for a two-year programme in Zimbabwe I couldn't believe my luck! I just couldn't wait to get away! I'd read up all I could find out about the country and I couldn't believe I was actually being sent out there to work with the children. I was so thrilled to think I had a chance of doing something worth while, some good in the world.

'I wouldn't have missed teaching the children in that remote little village for worlds.' She laughed. 'Even though it was an awful shock to discover the school day started at seven! But it was worth it! The children there are highly motivated, they want to learn. Some of them had to walk for two hours to attend the secondary school. Would you believe,' her voice rang with enthusiasm, 'that one third of my class were girls—not bad in a country where women are expected to walk one pace behind the man.'

'Really?' His cool tone left no doubt of his lack of interest in the subject of her voluntary service in the way of developing education in one of the world's poorest countries. 'So you made the big decision? Gave away the glamorous South Pacific cruise?'

'No!' She flung at him. 'You don't understand!' Why was she feeling so uptight with this stranger? 'The cruise was only postponed. When I accepted the offer to teach overseas Rick and I both knew it was only for a period, that we could go away on the boat later on.' Her voice was laced with enthusiasm. 'I had to make up my mind right then. I knew I might never again get a chance to take the position in Zimbabwe, or be free to accept it.' Why was she defending herself to this stranger? She didn't have to, did she? It didn't matter to her what this Craig character thought of her, how could it?

'And your Rick didn't raise any objections to your changing your mind at the last minute?' The mocking tones cut across her thoughts.

'Well no; that is,' she caught herself up, 'just at first, maybe.' Unbidden Rick's face flashed on the screen of her mind, his eyes dark with pain and shock and bewilderment. 'But I thought,' she had scarcely been able to catch the low tones, hoarse with anguish, 'that you were as mad as I am about cruising around the Pacific. You told me——'

'Oh, I know, I was looking forward to the trip—and then I got caught up in my own project——'

His mouth had tightened. 'You didn't let me in on all this.'

'I was going to as soon as I got definite word that I had been accepted for overseas work.' All at once her voice had rung with enthusiasm. 'And now I am! I got the letter today! I couldn't wait to tell you.'

'Why?' The flat tones had jerked her back to realisation that the fulfilment of her own private dream could mean the postponement of his.

'It's just something I want to do. I thought you'd be glad for me. You are?' she had asked tentatively. 'Aren't you?'

'What do *you* think?' The anger in his voice shocked her. 'All this time I've been planning on taking my girl on the adventure of a lifetime. Now it seems you're turning me down for a working holiday in some Godforsaken spot on the other side of the world!'

She had lifted her small chin. 'It's not a holiday!

And we'll take the trip together on the *Joanne* just as
we planned. It's postponed for a while, that's all!
We've got years and years ahead of us. It'll be
something to look forward to.' The bleakness of his
face touched her and her voice died into silence.

'Will it?'

It had taken a long time for her to talk him around
to her way of thinking but in the end he had agreed,
more or less reluctantly, to the two-year separation.
When had he ever refused her anything she wanted?
And he must know that the overseas work she had
been offered meant more to her than a Pacific ocean
cruise, more than being with him all the time, more
than anything else in the world!

'All I ask,' she had told him laughingly between his
kisses, 'is that you'll be at Rarotonga for our reunion.'

He had answered her in his serious, thoughtful way,
'When did I ever let you down?'

'So your friend decided to go it alone?' Craig's voice
jerked her back to the present.

'He didn't have to go alone!' She heard her
indignant tones rising high, a little out of control. 'He
had ever so many of his yachting club mates
clamouring for the chance to go alone with him, but
he preferred to go solo.'

'Bully for him!' She had an uneasy suspicion that
his bland tones conveyed a lot more he didn't say.
After a moment he asked carelessly, 'Tell me, just
how did you manage to talk him around to your point
of view?'

'Easy!' She turned a flushed face towards him. The
sense of elation was still with her and the words fell
from her lips unheedingly. 'Just at first he wasn't all
that pleased by my not going along on the cruise with
him, but I knew I'd get my own way in the end.'

Dimples flickered around the corners of her soft lips. 'I usually do.'

Craig was silent, his eyes cold and unreadable. But what matter if he didn't altogether approve of her? They were unlikely to meet again after tonight. He had a subtle way of putting her in the wrong, and before he could make a sarcastic comment—she just knew it would be sarcastic—she ran on. 'We arranged to meet up with each other on the first day of June this year. I could never make a mistake about that date.

'I only got back from Zimbabwe two days ago. Oh I could have got back a week earlier if I'd had a family, parents, someone to come home to, but there was no one around who——' she had been about to say 'cared' and substituted '—mattered'. 'So,' she shrugged slim shoulders, 'here I am.' She paused, eyeing him questioningly. 'You look surprised.'

'I am. What gets me is——' He broke off. 'Forget it. But why Rarotonga?'

'Oh, that,' Joanne laughed. In her present mood of elation it was easy to laugh. 'It just worked in. Rick reckoned that by the end of two years he'd have seen a lot of the Pacific Islands and Rarotonga was the last one on his itinerary.' She turned a sparkling face towards him. 'Do you wonder I'm so excited?'

When he made no comment she swept on, 'I'm booked in at the Rarotongan, the main hotel on the island. Do you know it?'

'Sure. It's a terrifice place to stay. Superb food, every possible attention and all the entertainment you could ever wish for thrown in. Go on.'

'Well, anyway, as soon as I got back to New Zealand I drew every cent I had from the bank. That covered my air-fare and I had enough money left, just, to keep me for seven days at the Rarotongan. Just in case there might be some delay in arrangements,' she confided. 'Who knows? Rick could strike a storm. Hurricanes and cyclones happen along a lot in the Pacific Islands. He could be wrecked on a reef or marooned on some little island no one has ever heard of.' All at once her tone lightened. 'But he promised me that nothing on earth would make him late for our appointment at Rarotonga so I don't think I need have any worries on that score. Even if something unforeseen did happen and I have to wait around for a few days until he turns up it won't worry me. I don't mind being alone.' She waited for the expected reaction to the statement that her vivacity, petite figure and appealing face inevitably evoked from newly acquainted young men: 'A girl like you—alone? You've got to be joking!'

It didn't come. Indeed Craig's impassive tones conveyed no more than a mild interest in her affairs. 'Heard from him lately, have you?' There was a penetrating gleam in the pale eyes. 'Lots of cards from ports of call, telegrams, telephone calls, all that stuff?'

She lifted her small chin, made her voice nonchalant, said carelessly, 'Not really.' And before he could make something of that, 'But I didn't expect to! When a man's staying as long as he wants to at groups of islands so tiny they're just dots on the map . . . Anyway,' she ran on defensively, 'Rick warned me about all that. Apart from postal difficulties, he's hopeless when it comes to letter-writing. Just doesn't get around to it.' Why was she trying to justify herself? She added lamely, 'The letters I sent him from Zimbabwe didn't reach him either.'

'How do you know?' He shot the words at her like bullets.

'Because he would have answered some of them.'

The next minute she could have bitten back the
words. 'Well, he might.'

She refused to meet Craig's mocking glance. But
what did his opinion matter? Nothing could alter the
love and trust between Rick and herself. Not absence,
not lack of communication, not anything! Craig was
cold and unfeeling, he just wouldn't be capable of
understanding the way she and Rick felt about each
other.

'You're not worried that your friend won't show up
at Rarotonga?'

She stared at him incredulously. 'Rick? Not turn up
for our special meeting on the island?' She didn't trust
one little bit the sardonic lift of his firmly cut lips. 'Of
course I'm not worried!' And immediately ruined the
effect of the words by saying, 'It would have to be
something utterly unforeseen that could stop him
meeting me. An act of God——'

'An act of God,' he echoed, and she caught the
sardonic look in his eyes. She suspected he was
laughing at her, critical about the special trust that she
and Rick had for each other. Well—she lifted her chin,
she seemed to be always lifting her chin
tonight—she'd prove to him how mistaken he was in
his snap judgement, that two people could really love
and trust each other, no matter what. She heard her
own voice saying defensively, challengingly, 'We're
planning, Rick and I, to get married on the island,
make a honeymoon of it.' His cynical expression
sparked her to say, 'You'll have to come to the
wedding!'

He merely shrugged broad shoulders.

Joanne's eyes glittered with annoyance. She was
determined to hit back at him for his obvious disbelief
in her faith in Rick's promise to meet her tomorrow.

She said challengingly, 'If you'd like to.'

The hint of steel was back in his eyes and nothing could be more off-hand than his cool tones. 'I'll let you know.'

She fumed inwardly. Suspicious brute, she told herself. It's not what he says but what he doesn't say. Cynical, disbelieving . . . She had thought him attractive at first sight, his lean athletic frame and strong face were enough to attract any girl's attention. But that was before she knew what he was really like.

'When did you last hear from him?' His staccato tones jerked her from her angry musing.

'Rick? Oh, it was ages ago. Eight and a half months.' The next moment she would have given anything to recall the words. Damn! Now she had betrayed herself by letting him know she had kept count of the time since Rick's last letter. For sure he would make something of that! 'But it doesn't mean a thing!' she ran on airily. 'I was prepared for that, we both were. He'll be there to meet me at the airport when we get to the island, you'll see!'

'Look,' the oddly serious note in his voice took her by surprise, 'if things don't work out, if you happen to run into any delays, problems, financial, whatever, you can get in touch with me at any time.' He regarded her with his penetrating look. 'Don't forget.'

'Problems?' She stared at him in disbelief. 'But it's going to be wonderful for me, a dream come true. A honeymoon in a Pacific paradise. What more could a girl want?'

He ignored that. She might just as well have been speaking to herself, she thought crossly.

'Just ring the Kia Orana. It's a motel on the other side of the island from the Rarotongan. You can get in touch with me any time, day or night. There'll be

someone there to take the call. Ask for Craig, Craig
Summers. I'll be around.' His sudden smile
illuminated his strong tanned features. 'Right,
Joanne?'

'Don't worry about me.' She had scarcely taken in
what he had been saying. 'For heaven's sake, if
anything did go wrong with our arrangements, and I
know it won't, there'd be time enough then to worry.'
She tried for lightness. 'If the impossible happened
and Rick did happen to be a week or two late in arriving, I can always try for a chef's job at one of the
hotels on the island. Funny, isn't it,' she confided,
'after I left High School I took a cordon bleu course in
cookery, but I've never had a chance to use it. Too
busy teaching, I guess, and then doing the Voluntary
Services work that meant so much to me.'

'Pity.'

Once again he appeared to have lost interest in
details of her work with underprivileged children on
the other side of the world. As for herself, the name of
the motel where Craig would be staying had scarcely
registered with her. But what matter? She wouldn't
need help from anyone on the island. Ridiculous
thought!

To change the subject she said idly, 'You'll be
staying on the island for a while then?'

'As from tonight.' Now it was his voice that had
become charged with enthusiasm. 'For good,
actually.' There was a note of immense satisfaction in
his voice.

'Really?' She eyed him in surprise. 'You know the
island well?'

He grinned. 'Should do. I spent school holidays
there with my uncle when I was a kid and from then
on I sort of got the habit. He owned property on the

island. It's a bit off the beaten track but there's a lagoon with a great swimming-beach.' All at once his face was shadowed, his tone tinged with regret. 'I sure miss the old boy now that he's gone.'

'Your uncle owned land on the island?' Her piquant face wore a puzzled expression. 'Someone who had lived there told me that the island is so small and land there so precious to the Rarotongans that it can't be bought by anyone. That it's only passed on through family relationships. Sometimes it's cut up into small lots at that. But no stranger can buy the land.'

'True.'

She stared up at him. 'But your uncle——'

'I'm only a relation of his by marriage, but he owned the land all right!' His well-shaped lips quirked. 'Way back his grandfather was captain of a sailing ship that used to call in at Rarotonga from England once a year to unload supplies and pick up a cargo of copra and pearl-shell. Old Great Uncle Joshua was so taken with the island life-style that he tossed in his command and came back to Rarotonga to marry the native girl he'd fallen in love with on his last voyage out.' He grinned again. 'A bit tough on the vicar's daughter in Yorkshire he'd been engaged to for four years. But you can't really blame the old boy, not when you see how attractive the local girls are. Besides, it's a sort of paradise, the island. You don't need much money to enjoy the good life. Tropical fruit grows wild all over the place, you just help yourself when you feel like it. Locals can dig a few potatoes from their garden plot if they want some extra cash but there isn't much to buy with it except motor scooters. You'll see plenty of them on the island. Tomatoes grow all the year round, paw-paw, bananas, pineapple, grow everywhere and there's breadfruit and taro. The islanders are practically self-supporting, there's always fish to catch in the lagoon. Houses are adequate and cheap and that's it. And the kapok tree supplies the wherewithal for one mattress a year.

'It's such a small island, the road runs around the edge of the sea so there's nowhere particular to go. you can ride your push-bike or walk right around it. The sun shines most days and the soft, warm rain grows all the food they need like crazy.'

Joanne, however, was thinking back to what he had told her about his own property. 'You inherited land on the island from your uncle, you said?'

'That's right. He gave me a lease on it for years and years.'

Her gaze went to the flat leather case where he had packed away the architectural drawings she had seen him perusing at the start of the flight. 'And you've got plans for it?'

'Have I ever!' All at once his steely eyes were alight with interest. 'Hotel management, tourism, all that happens to be my line of country. For years I've had ideas in the back of my mind for a motel here on the island. Now they're for real—or just about. I was lucky. It's a block of land, big enough to take ten self-contained units. Look, if you can picture it——'

Taking a ballpoint from his pocket he sketched on a scrap of paper an impression of land sloping down to a lagoon. 'These are the motel units. I can't build any higher than a coconut tree by law.'

Joanne was only too glad to switch the conversation from her own affairs. 'Tell me about it.' Leaning towards him, her dark curls brushing his cheek, she caught the clean tang of male cologne aftershave. And then it happened. Their glances meshed and tiny fires burned deep in his eyes. For a crazy moment a life-force, electricity, potent and coming from nowhere, held them. Then with an effort she wrenched her gaze aside. She said shakily, 'You were saying——'

She must have imagined that look in his eyes, she told herself. How crazy could you get? It was the effect of the dark, star-ridden night, the intimacy of the crowded seat, her own mood of high elation, what else?

His matter-of-fact tones calmed her rioting thoughts. 'I'm putting up the units with families in mind. A place where they can be comfortable, get their own meals if they want to. I'm aiming to put together a resort combining limited cooking facilities with a café and house bar. Suites for discerning clients. A small personal property with resort-type activities and seven-day on-site management. Catering for honeymooners, first time around or second. How does all that strike you?'

She had scarcely taken in what he had been telling her.

'Sounds fine to me.'

'The place is right near the lagoon for reef-walking and there'll be all sorts or activities to suit everyone in the family,' he went on. 'Snorkelling, wind-surfing, shell-collecting, fishing, or they can sail around the lagoon in a dinghy. I've put in a pool and I've left all the trees I could for shade and fruit-picking. Now there's only the restaurant to be completed,' his voice rang with pride, 'and that should be open for business in a week's time. I'm planning to make it a place where food is just a bit different, not just the run-of-the-mill variety but tastefully served meals with menus made up of fruit and vegetables grown right here on the island. I'm aiming for distinctive recipes featuring local produce.

'But that's fantastic! I wonder,' she mused, 'why more tourist hotels and restaurants in tropical places don't use the fruit growing wild everywhere around them.'

'I'm working on it,' he told her. 'For starters I've heard there's a cookery book on the island made up by women of the local church organisations. It could be mighty interesting and suit my purposes.'

'I bet it would! Would you show it to me when you get one?'

Once again a quizzical expression crossed his face. 'If you haven't more interesting things to do with your time than boning up on how to cook guavas or marinate a fish in coconut cream.'

She decided to let that go. 'I take it, then, that you're almost ready to welcome your guests?'

'That's right! I'm lucky in being able to employ local girls who've worked at that type of job. They're a happy, cheerful lot with loads of common sense.'

'Will there be a courtesy car to transport tourists from the airport and back?'

'I've got one jacked up. It's got swags of rust on the bodywork like every other vehicle on the island but the engine's got plenty of oomph and there's lots of comfortable seating.'

Some of his enthusiasm was brushing off on her. 'How about a chef for your restaurant? You'll need a top-class one.'

'Don't I know it! The guy I've got in mind is between jobs but he's being offered incredible salaries by high-class New Zealand restaurants at the ski resorts down south. I'm doing my best to talk him into working for me, trying to persuade him that the island sunshine makes up for a lot. He'll have to get

used to the relaxed way of life over here. Everyone at
Rarotonga works on "island" time. Tomorrow, next
week, next month, what does it matter?' He shot her a
cool glance from too-perceptive pale eyes. 'Just giving
you fair warning.'

Instantly she was on the defensive. 'I hope you're
not trying to tell me that Rick might not turn up at the
island for ages,' her eyes flashed danger signals,
'because if you are, let me tell you something. You
don't know him as I do.' She added on an angry
breath, 'You'll see.'

'Great. Let me know when I can expect the big
reunion.'

A hot tide of resentment surged over her. How ever
could she have thought him attractive? But that was
before she had got to know his real nature. Cold,
censorious, autocratic. Clearly he had never loved a
girl the way Rick loved her. A worried frown creased
her forehead and she nibbled at her thumb nail.

'*Now* what's wrong?' His piercing eyes seemed to
miss nothing, she thought crossly.

You! But she bit back the angry words that
trembled on her lips. Instead she said huffily,
'Nothing, nothing at all.'

She couldn't stand the man! It was absurd the way
he seemed to view her and Rick's separation
—correction, temporary separation. Why, he
appeared almost to regard her as a self-centred,
ruthlessly determined female who achieved her own
ends at whatever cost, regardless of the feelings of
others, even when it came to the man who loved her.
He was so wrong! As he would find out in the next
few days, when he saw her and Rick together. That,
she thought fiercely, would show him! She could
hardly wait for her moment of triumph.

All at once she realised that the cabin lights were dimmed, and presently the buzz of conversation died away as passengers settled down and tried to sleep.

Joanne adjusted her seat-belt, leaned back and closed her eyes. Don't think of the disturbing man at your side. Think of Rick. It was funny, but tonight she was finding it difficult to recall his face in any detail.

The droning of the engines and the warmth of the cabin lulled her into a sense of relaxation. Not long now. She and Rick would have so much time to make up. She knew she wouldn't sleep, she never did drop off on long plane journeys, but at least she could give herself some respite from her companion's unwelcome interference in her affairs.

At some time during the night she was vaguely aware of a blanket being tucked gently around her shoulders, then once again oblivion claimed her. She must have dozed off after all, though, for the next thing of which she was aware was struggling through mists of sleep and a blissful sensation of utter comfort. She didn't want ever to wake up, not when she was feeling so happy, so dreamily content, nestling close to . . . Realisation returned with a rush and she jerked herself to a sitting position, aware that Craig's arm had been gently withdrawn from around her shoulders. Stung with mortification, she realised she had been pressed close to his strong, warm body, happily close, for goodness knew how long.

A sideways glance showed her that Craig too was awake. He looked younger, more human, she decided, his dark hair tousled and falling over his forehead, his shirt rumpled. Rumpled because of her?

'I was dead asleep,' she offered inadequately.

'So,' he murmured ruefully, 'is my arm.'

'Sorry about that.' She avoided his gaze. 'You

should have pushed me back to my own seat.'

For a second his pale eyes were almost human, something flickering in their depths. 'Why should I? I was enjoying it immensely, especially——'

'Especially?' She did her best to glare at him but she was finding it difficult with hair flying around her face every which way, her blouse dishevelled and sandals lying somewhere beneath her seat.

'You don't remember?' he enquired blandly.

She stared at him incredulously. 'I haven't a clue what you're on about!' She shook the cluster of curls back from her forehead and tried to gather together her confused senses. She wouldn't, she couldn't—he was making all this up just to annoy her.

'Don't worry about it!' His eyes still had that devilish glint. 'Thought you were away with your Rick on a tropical island, I expect that's what it was. Amazing what folks get up to when they're dead to the world! Wishful thinking, I guess. Oh well, blame it on your boyfriend!'

A panicky feeling was winging its way down her spine. Just what had she done during those hours of oblivion?

She glared at him fiercely. 'You're having me on!'

'Me?' He was regarding her with his pale stare. 'Why would I do that?'

'I'll tell you why!' she flashed back. 'Oh, I know how you men stick together and you've got some crazy notion that I've let Rick down. Well, let me put you right. We——'

'Good morning!' The air hostess, smiling and cheerful and looking incredibly fresh and immaculate after the long night, had paused beside them with her trolley of food.

Thankful for the interruption that put an end to the

ridiculous argument with Craig, Joanne flipped down her plastic table with an angry jerk.

'My goodness.' Turning towards him, she tried for lightness. 'Is this breakfast?' She glanced down at her tiny gold wristwatch. 'At three in the morning?'

His tone was matter-of-fact. 'We've only got an hour's flying time to go before we hit the airport at Rarotonga. Pleased?'

Was she pleased? After a night spent with him as her travelling companion? She threw him a tight-lipped glance. 'What do *you* think?'

CHAPTER TWO

THE small international airport was a blaze of light in the intense darkness of the island night. Joanne, stepping down from the plane into the warm, perfumed air, was all but unaware of her surroundings, her eager gaze sweeping the groups waiting below for Rick's tall frame and bearded face.

Swiftly she threaded her way among the flower-garlanded Rarotongans waiting to welcome back friends and relatives arriving from the New Zealand plane that had just touched down at the airport. Indeed, it seemed to Joanne that everyone living on the island must be here, except Rick.

'*Kia Orana!* Welcome to Rarotonga!' A smiling, olive-skinned girl slipped a long fragrant lei of blossoms around Joanne's shoulders.

'Thank you.' She threw the girl a smile but she was scarcely aware of the freshly gathered flowers, satiny sweet-scented frangipani, tiny purple orchids, white daisies with their spicy fragrance.

Idiot! she chided herself, to feel this stirring of unease just because Rick wasn't here to meet her. He would be waiting for her at the hotel. Of course that was the explanation for his absence. When had he ever let her down?

A short time later, with formalities completed, she gave a last backward glance among the crowd pressing around her, then she turned away to join passengers who were climbing into the courtesy car sent by the

hotel. A swift glance inside the vehicle assured her that
Craig wasn't there. Thank heaven for that! At last she
was free of his disturbing presence. Probably they
wouldn't meet again, certainly not if she could help it!
No doubt he would be involved in his project on the
other side of the island from the hotel. Anyway, she
brought her random thoughts up with a jerk, why was
she thinking of him? The answer came unbidden.
Because he was annoying and interfering and generally
insufferable, that was why!

Determinedly she switched her thoughts aside and
glanced out of the window. The coach had left the
friendly airport behind and was now taking a dark road.
In the pre-dawn dimness she could make out nothing
but the blur of bushes crowding the roadway and the
silhouettes of tall coconut palms reaching drunkenly for
the sky.

Some time later the minibus swept around a bend to
meet a blaze of lights beaming out into the darkness.
Soon the vehicle was sweeping into a courtyard studded
with flowering hibiscus bushes to draw up at the wide-
open entrance doors of the hotel.

Joanne gained an impression of paper lanterns
hanging like fragile moons from a high-peaked ceiling
and of tropical greenery cascading from coconut-
matting-covered walls.

Olive-skinned youths plucked at their singing guitars
and a dark-eyed girl wearing a coronet of flowers in her
flowing black tresses moved forward to greet Joanne
with a smile of welcome and a glass of chilled paw-paw
juice from a great carved wooden bowl.

Joanne shook her head and hurried towards the long
counter with its scattering of scarlet hibiscus blossoms.
'Please,' she appealed to a youth standing behind the
counter, 'I'm Joanne Daley.' The words tumbled over

one another in her excitement. 'Tell me, is there a guest staying here named Mason? Rick Mason?'

'I will check for you,' came the soft island accents. He reached towards a sheet of typewritten names, then turned back to her. 'No.' She thought the liquid dark eyes held a bewildered expression. Maybe he didn't understand what she had asked him. Had she been speaking too fast in her excitement? Carefully she enunciated the query, 'Rick, Rick Mason? You couldn't help but notice him,' she ran on, 'he's awfully tall and thin with a sandy-coloured beard. That is, he had a beard when I saw him last. Maybe now——' Her voice died away uncertainly.

'I am sorry.' A sympathetic shake of his dark head. 'He is not staying at this hotel. Would he have come on tonight's plane?'

'No, no, he wasn't on the plane.' All at once her tone was laced with urgency, her eyes anxious. 'A message, then? There *must* be a message waiting here for me.'

'I will enquire.' Obligingly the desk-clerk turned towards the letter-rack behind him and riffled through a compartment. 'There is nothing here for you. I will ask the hostess, she may know of something.'

'Please.'

Joanne waited as he approached a pleasant-faced woman of middle age wearing a flowing cotton frock patterned in motifs of sea-shells. He was back with her almost at once. 'I am sorry.' He shook his head.

Disappointment and a sickening sense of let-down made her give voice to her thoughts. 'But there *must* be!' she cried. 'I'm sure he would have left some word for me. He was to meet me here tonight! He promised!'

'Maybe,' came the soft island accents, 'your friend is booked in at some other hotel on the island. There are motels——'

'No! He told me he would meet me here at the Rarotongan.' She stopped short, all at once aware of travel-weary faces that were crowding around her. Clearly the new arrivals were waiting to obtain keys to their apartments and becoming impatient of the delay.

She had left the counter when the youth called after her, 'Miss Daley, here is your key. Your unit is along the walkway on the left and up the steps.'

'Thank you.' Dispiritedly she turned away, her eyes misted with unshed tears.

A soft wind rustled the palm trees as she took the softly lighted path winding amongst flowering frangipani bushes, hibiscus and yellow trumpet lilies. But she was unaware of her surroundings, her disappointment was so intense. Rick, where are you?

'Joanne! Wait!' An all-too-familiar masculine voice jerked her back to the present. Pretending not to have heard Craig's call, she quickened her footsteps. Wouldn't you know, she told herself with tightly compressed lips, that he would be right here on the walkway, his long strides rapidly catching up with her.

'Any luck?'

Swiftly she dashed the moisture from her eyes with the back of her hand and flung around to face him. As if he cared whether or not Rick were waiting here for her! She said with an attempt at bravado, 'I don't know what you're on about.'

'Don't give me that! You got no joy from the desk-clerk about—what was his name?' As if he didn't know. 'Rick, wasn't it?'

Swiftly she put on her brightest smile, the 'couldn't-care-less' one. 'Not really.' And she ran on before he could make one of his horribly perceptive comments. 'But I'm not worrying, why should I? Anything could have happened to hold him up for a day or so.'

'Well, don't let it throw you,' he said cheerfully, and she wondered, had it been the quiver in her voice that had betrayed her inner anxiety?

As they moved on together, their footsteps noiseless on the soft ground of the track, he said carelessly, 'You've still got a bit of time up your sleeve.'

'I haven't, you know!' She eyed him indignantly.

'Aren't you forgetting something?' He seemed to take a fiendish delight in torturing her.

'I haven't the faintest idea what you're getting at,' she said coldly.

'I'll let you into the good news, then!' The satirical note was back in his voice. 'We crossed the International Date Line, when you were asleep. Remember?'

Did she remember! Asleep in his arms for hours! Oh, he was maddening.

'Thursday, June the first,' he was saying, 'when we left Auckland. And now we're here it's still Thursday, June the first. Somewhere between here and there we've lost a day. Pleased?'

Enlightenment dawned on her. 'Of course! Why didn't I think of that?' All at once her smile was for real, warm and radiant.

They climbed the timber steps leading up to the units above. 'Number thirty, that's me!' She paused to unlock the door of the lighted apartment, then turned a sparkling face in his direction. She was almost light-headed with relief. She could even tolerate, just, her interfering, know-all companion. 'Just think! I'll be seeing Rick again—tomorrow.'

'You reckon?' came the cool satirical voice at her side. 'I wouldn't bet on it!' He left her to move towards the door of the adjoining apartment.

'I would!' she called after him. 'Any time!' But he had moved inside and closed the door behind him.

In the cool attractive lounge room with its olive-green décor and cane furniture, she tossed her travel bag on a chair and pulled back the drapes from floor-to-ceiling windows to reveal a spectacular sunrise. Streaks of rose and orange painted the eastern sky. Below tall coconut palms framed a view of turquoise-coloured water, spray tossed high in the air where waves dashed against the coral reef.

Presently, when she had showered and slipped into bra and panties, she took from her travel bag the peach-coloured linen sunfrock she hadn't worn since last summer. She brushed her hair vigorously until it sprang back in waves and curls, then she added a touch of mascara to her lashes. A smudge of blue eyeshadow and she was ready for the day. The interminable day that stretched ahead.

Snatching up her capacious beach-bag, she checked the contents. Bikini and sunglasses, sunburn lotion, sunblock cream, a romance paperback. Although however she was going to concentrate on reading today she couldn't imagine. She decided she would spend the day on the beach, swimming in the sea within the reef, lounging on golden sands, letting the sun have its way with her winter-pale body.

A glance towards the adjoining unit showed her that Craig's door was closed. No doubt he would soon be taking himself off to his own domain. Almost she wished he would still be around tomorrow when Rick arrived at the hotel. That would wipe the sardonic look from Craig's steely blue eyes, teach him a lesson about making snap judgements regarding a man he hadn't even met. Busy with her thoughts she moved along the winding walkway with its borders of pink hibiscus blossoms and trailing vines starred with great yellow trumpet flowers burnished to gold in the hot sunshine.

In the dining-room where great bunches of bananas hung from high rafters in the peaked ceiling, she helped herself from long tables with their tempting array of tropical fruits—sliced pineapple, squares of coconut, luscious golden paw-paw. Then she moved to seat herself at a white wrought-iron table beside the pool.

A family party seated at an adjoining table called a friendly 'Good morning!' and Joanne responded with a smile. Somehow it was easy to be nice to everyone this morning. Could it be the sound of Kiwi accents echoing all around her that gave her a pleasant feeling of familiarity, she mused, and wondered if Rick would feel the same way when he sailed into port tomorrow.

I'll stick around the beach all day, she told herself happily, just in case Rick happens to arrive here a day earlier than we planned. Suddenly she couldn't wait for tomorrow to be with him again.

She finished her coffee and soon she was making her way towards the crystal-clear water, the drifts of golden sand already warm to the touch of her bare feet.

She swam lazily in water that seemed to caress her body, splashing out at intervals to drop down on the sand, to return again and again to the relaxing yet bracing touch of the sea.

Later she went to a nearby booth to get snorkel and mask from the beach hut and soon she was swimming out to the coral reef, enraptured by the sight of the small jewelled fish gliding by in the sheltered waters of the reef.

She threw occasional glances towards the shore. Rick could arrive here a day early, she told herself. Well, he might.

The hours slipped by more swiftly than she had anticipated and at last she picked up her towel, rubbed the seawater from her streaming hair and made her way to the main building. It was as she passed a small shop with its displays of pearls, rose-coloured coral jewellery, woven sun hats, shell necklaces and gleaming eel-skin handbags that she noticed racks hung with lengths of soft cotton, tie-dyed and printed in motifs of vividly coloured tropical blossoms, sea creatures and shells. A notice-board advised guests to wear the native *pareu* as dinner would be served *omu* style, the food cooked all afternoon in native earth ovens.

Why not wear a *pareu?* From a colourful assortment Joanne chose a length of lilac-shaded cotton patterned with white seashells.

'Let me show you how to tie the garment,' offered a smiling young attendant. 'There are so many ways.' Draping the material around Joanne's slim body, she knotted the garment beneath the arms.

Joanne couldn't help feeling surprised and delighted with the result. The soft muslin falling around her ankles was a joy to wear and she had a swift mental picture of Rick's appreciative gaze should he happen to walk into the hotel dining-room tonight in search of her. She just knew this was the way he would like her to greet him, Pacific Islands style!

Carried away with the thought, she purchased two more lengths of material, one dyed in shadings of coral and the other in muted tones of blue and green. Then she made her way back to her room to shower away the salt from her hair and to make herself ready for the night's entertainment.

Knotting the *pareu* in just the right places took quite a long time but at last she achieved it to her satisfaction. She enjoyed wearing the *pareu,* she decided. Tonight she looked—different—she mused happily. The strapless garment falling to her ankles was cool and infinitely becoming. Rick wouldn't be disappointed in her appearance after two years' separation. Her bare shoulders were softly flushed from the effects of sun and sand and sea-water, and the apricot-tan of her cheeks seemed to make her eyes appear even more vividly blue than usual. Her hair, dark and silky, had taken on a life of its own, waving and curling around her face.

Guitars throbbed softly through the big room as Joanne entered the dining-area. Soon she was joining in the long line of guests who were making their way slowly along the long hibiscus-scattered tables with their appetising array of dishes. Locally grown vegetables, pumpkin and kumera, chicken, mutton and pork cooked to succulent tenderness in earth ovens were arranged on green leaves on wooden platters.

Joanne, moving slowly along the tables with their tempting variety of salads, paused to eye a plate heaped with small, silvery green morsels that were unfamiliar to her. Well, she decided, she'd give anything a go, and leaned forward to pick up on her fork a tiny green spear.

'Sure you want it?' enquired a maddening masculine voice at her side. 'You won't care for it, you know!'

She spun around, wide-eyed. 'Oh, no! Not——'

He grinned, the heart-knocking smile that seemed to do things to her composure. A habit she seemed unable to get the better of once again betrayed her and she spoke the first words that sprang into her mind. 'I thought you'd gone!'

Too late, she realised she had played right into his hands.

'You missed me!'

Wildly she searched her mind, but she couldn't come up with a sufficiently cutting retort. Instead she stabbed viciously at the tiny green spear on her plate. 'Can you tell me what this is?'

'Sure. It's a type of seaweed.'

'Oh!' Somehow her appetite for the odd-looking spears had fled but she would eat it, she vowed, even if it killed her. In an attempt to forestall any personal questions from him, she indicated a platter heaped with what looked to her like potato chips but slightly different. 'And these are——?'

'Arrowroot spears.' His gaze moved along the platters on the table. 'And here we have raw clams, cooked clams, tuna, octopus, taro, rakau——'

'Rakau? What's that?'

'Taro leaves marinated in coconut cream. You'll really go for that one!'

'I'll give it a miss.' Something about his autocratic attitude concerning her tastes in food put her on the defensive, made her determined to ignore his advice in the matter of food. Or anything else for that matter. Especially, she told herself fiercely, when it came to anything connected with her personal life—and Rick!

'Up to you,' he was saying equably. 'Now right here we have desserts. This——'

'I know what it is,' she snapped. 'Mango in a melon shell!'

As they moved along the temptingly arranged foods, plates in their hands, a waiter came to join them. 'Let me show you to your seats.'

What could she do? There was nothing for it, she thought helplessly, but to go along with Craig as they were guided to a candlelit table where wide windows looked out on the beach.

When they were seated she gazed around the colourful scene and unconsciously she sighed. Her first dinner here at the hotel was just the way she had dreamed it would be. The music, the food, the seting, it was all perfect. Only Craig spoiled the picture, made everything disappointingly different. If only it were Rick who was seated opposite her.

Craig was busy with the wine waiter and she slanted him a glance. She had to admit that, in contrast with most of the men in the big room, he appeared to be perfectly at ease in the colourful island garb, as no doubt he was. His cream cotton shirt with its motifs of sea-horses was open at the throat, revealing a sun-browned chest and a mat of thick dark hair. A sneaky voice in her mind whispered that, regardless of what he wore, Craig would inevitably be the most attention-getting male in the room. A man of hard-muscled strength, lithe and tall and vibrantly alive, he was almost unbearably attractive. She sensed about him a male magnetism so potent that if she hadn't known the type of person he really was—swiftly she caught herself up, aghast at the direction in which her thoughts were drifting.

The waiter brought a carafe of wine and Craig raised his glass, the lazy glint in his eyes oddly unnerving. 'To your big reunion!'

She ignored the irony in his tones. 'I'll drink to that!'

'Whenever it is!' There he went again, she thought hotly, spoiling everything, trying to shake her faith in Rick's promise to meet her here.

'Tomorrow!' she said firmly as their glasses clinked. All at once her spirits rose and her blue eyes sparkled with challenge as she met his satirical glance. But that she found was a mistake. There was something about his gaze that was turning her world upside down. With an effort she wrenched her glance aside, and began to chatter of unimportant things.

Soon the spacious room echoed with the buzz of conversation and snatches of laughter rose above the pulsing beat of guitars.

Much later a young man took the stage, singing an island love song in a voice that could touch the heart. Or could it be, Joanne asked herself, that tonight she was intensely vulnerable to romantic music, filled with a sense of elation, a wild happiness? And why not, when she would be seeing Rick in only a few hours' time?

The singer left the stage and a group of island dancers took his place. Like a clap of thunder came the wild clamour of the beat of wooden drums. Men and women, leis of blossoms flying around bare shoulders, dark hair wreathed in coronets of flowers and coconut fibre skirts flying as they moved to the blood-stirring sensuous rhythm.

The beat of drums was intoxicating, the men's knees moving faster and faster to the compelling sounds, the women's hips, accentuated by wide bands of green leaves, rotating in a frenzy of movement.

Joanne was fascinated by the wild rhythm. 'Isn't it terrific!' Her eyes were shining with excitement.

'Why don't we give it a go?' Craig had risen to his feet and was eyeing her expectantly.

She hesitated. 'I've never tried island dancing.'

'Nothing to it,' he assured her. 'Come on, I'll show you how.'

That did it. 'No, thanks,' she said shortly.

'You know something?' His resonant tones were very persuasive, but she steeled herself against him. 'You can't do that!'

'Do what?' She eyed him questioningly. He had a disconcerting way of making her feel confused, darn him.

'Turn me down for a dance. It's just not done, not on Rarotonga. The islanders consider it a deadly insult for a girl to turn a man down.'

She eyed him suspiciously, not knowing whether or not to believe what he was telling her. 'But you're not an islander,' she pointed out.

'I am, you know.' His beguiling tones were hard to
resist. 'As I told you, as from today.'

'Oh, all right, then!' She kicked off her rubber jandals
and moved barefooted with him as they joined the
couples who were moving up to the stage to become a
part of the scintillating throng. Swiftly Joanne emulated
the island dancers and in no time at all she fell into the
sensuous rhythm of the beating drums. Her face was
flushed, her dark hair falling in curls and tendrils around
her damp forehead, when at last the dance came to an
end.

She said breathlessly, 'That was terrific!'

He grinned. 'And I thought I'd have to give you a
dancing lesson!'

But she had had enough of his high-handed ways, his
knack of managing somehow always to put her in the
wrong. She lifted her small chin, contrived a nonchalant
smile. 'As you said, there's nothing to it!'

'Joanne——' All at once his tone was serious, but he
said no more. Suddenly she felt as though she were
drowning, out of her depth and powerless beneath the
spell of his magnetic gaze.

'It's getting awfully late,' she muttered. Why was she
breathing hard? Put it down to the wild rhythm of the
dance. She pushed the tumbled hair back from her
forehead. 'I'd better be getting back.' She bent to
retrieve her rubber jandals lying under her chair. 'I've
got to be fresh for tomorrow.'

He ignored that. Getting to his feet, he said, 'I'll see
you back to the unit.'

'Don't bother.'

'No bother.' His tone was as cool and off-hand as ever,
and she wondered if she had imagined that crazy
moment of awareness.

She could have sworn that he had felt it too, but then

he was the type of man who was adept at hiding his feelings, if he had any feelings! She must have merely fancied the sudden tiny lights that had flickered for a moment in his steely blue eyes.

At the door of her unit he left her. 'Night.'

'Bye.' As she unlocked her door and went inside the apartment she found herself hoping that he would still be here tomorrow. If only so that she could prove to him how mistaken he had been in his opinion of Rick—and herself. All at once it seemed important that he should realise how right she had been in her decision to insist on the two-year separation that would all turn out as she and Rick had planned. She couldn't wait to gain her victory over Craig—tomorrow!

CHAPTER THREE

THE next morning Joanne awoke to bright sunlight streaming into the room. Vaguely she was aware of the booming of the surf on the coral reef nearby, together with a dreamy sensation that this was the day on which wonderful things would be happening. The next minute reality returned with a rush. Of course—Rick!

From outside her room came bursts of feminine laughter interspersed with the soft singing of the young island housemaids. Joanne felt like singing herself on this golden sunshiny morning.

Presently she was wrapping around her slim body the length of sea-green material she had purchased at the hotel shop. Knotting the garment in just the right places took her quite a while but in the end she was pleased with her mirrored reflection.

The loosely fitting garment was cool and infinitely becoming. Her bare shoulders were flushed from yesterday's touch of sea and sand and salt water and the golden tan of her cheeks seemed to make her eyes appear even more blue than usual. Even her hair, dark and silky, seemed to have taken on a life of its own, curling in waves and ringlets around her face and down to her shoulders. She looked . . . different. Like a girl in love. And why not?

Soon she was slipping out of the room and into a blaze of sunshine where below the balcony every leaf and blossom glistened in the clear warm air. A sparkling morning, especially for her!

All at once she realised that he door of the adjoining unit stood open and inside the room the maids were busy with their whisks and brooms as they prepared the apartment for the next occupant. So Craig had left the hotel. For no reason at all a shaft of dismay pierced her. And he hadn't even said goodbye!

For heaven's sake, she chided herself the next moment, why should he? They had shared a seat on the plane from New Zealand, attended an island dinner together. Nothing things. Why, they didn't even like each other, not one little bit! Merely being in each other's company sparked all sorts of emotional conflict between them. She was glad he had gone. Good riddance! The only reason she was feeling this odd sense of let-down was that she had been looking forward so much to her moment of triumph when Rick joined her here today. Trust Craig to cheat her out of her big moment of satisfaction—of proving to him that he didn't know a thing about a man and a woman in love with each other. She brought her resentful thoughts up with a jerk. Forget him. Don't let him spoil the day, this special day. She was unlikely to see him again, thank heaven for that.

She strolled along the winding walkway with its flowering bushes and tropical fruit on the trees, then went to the reception desk to enquire if there had been a message left there for her. This time she half expected a negative answer to her query. For why should Rick leave a message for her when he would be here himself some time during the day?

It was unthinkable, she mused as she climbed the steps leading to the dining-room, that Rick could forget the date, not that particular one. We must truly love one another a lot or we wouldn't have stayed together so many years, never wanting anyone else, perfectly content with each other's company. Friends as well as lovers. And she wondered why she had to assure herself of something that went without saying. Blame Craig, she thought crossly, for putting doubts in my mind, or trying to, taking a fiendish delight in throwing cold water on all my hopes and dreams.

She would breakfast by the pool in the sunshine, she decided, then return to the flower-decorated reception-room. That way, she would be ready and waiting to run to meet Rick the moment he came hurrying in at the entrance. She just knew the way he would look, fit and tanned, his eyes filled with love and longing for her.

Only, she thought on a sigh some hours later, it was a very long time to wait. Never had she known the hours pass so slowly. In the spacious room guests came and went, cars, taxis and tour coaches pulled in at the flower-studded courtyard. After the arrival of the first three vehicles Joanne restrained herself from hurrying eagerly to the hotel entrance.

She skipped lunch, for what did food matter compared with the importance of being right here to greet Rick the moment he arrived at the hotel?

A long time later, when shadows had lengthened in the courtyard and still Rick hadn't made an appearance, she willed herself to be patient. The day wasn't yet ended—or the night for that matter!

All at once she realised that guests and staff were beginning to cast curious glances towards the girl who sat alone, eyes ever alerted to the entrance doors where tour buses and cars discharged passengers before driving away. Like the family group who had occupied an adjoining poolside table at breakfast time.

'Oh, hello! Still here?' A young woman with wind-tossed hair and an open friendly face paused at her side with her husband and small son. 'We had a fabulous trip today. We hired a car and went right around the island, finished up with a swim in the lagoon. It didn't take all that long.' She broke off. Something of the look of strain evident in Joanne's face must have got through to her. 'You haven't been waiting here *all day?*' All at once her sunburned face wore an expression of concern. 'There's nothing wrong, is there?'

'No, no, of course not.' Joanne forced a smile to her lips. 'I'm expecting a friend.' She made her voice light and confident. 'He'll be along any minute now.'

'Oh.' The kindly face relaxed. 'That's all right then. See you at dinner.' She turned away.

Joanne had no appetite for the evening meal. She would stay right here, she told herself, and once Rick arrived . . .

The slow hours dragged by and now there was only one other occupant of the room, a young Rarotongan youth standing behind the flower-strewn counter. Joanne recognised the friendly clerk from whom she had made enquiries about Rick when she first arrived at the hotel.

At that moment he moved towards her, a solicitous expression in his soft, dark eyes. 'Is there anything I can do for you?'

Joanne shook her head. 'No, thank you. I'm just waiting for someone. He's been delayed but he won't be long now.' Even to her own ears the words had a hollow ring.

At some time near morning she must have dozed off for she awoke with a start, feeling cramped and cold. Dazedly she was aware of the Rarotongan clerk gazing down at her and she was all too conscious of an expression of concern in his eyes. Sympathy? Pity? That she couldn't endure.

She pushed the dark mop of curls away from her eyes. 'I must have dropped off.' She sent him a smile that was near enough to the real thing. 'I think I'll call it a day—or a night.'

He continued to eye her gravely. 'Do not worry. I will let you know if a message is sent to you or if your friend comes.'

If! Worse and worse. Her stomach seemed to churn. 'Thanks.' She nodded and made her way through the dawn light to her apartment, turning the key with shaking fingers.

Dropping down to the bed, she felt the tears well behind her eyelids. Don't be stupid, she admonished herself. Just because Rick isn't here on this special day we arranged to meet, it's not to say he won't come. You know he has been sailing on his yacht and you're well aware of the things that could happen to delay him. He could be becalmed somewhere in the Pacific, he wouldn't take an engine on the boat, remember? He wanted to depend on the sails. You know what that could mean in the way of delays. He could easily have come to grief, been wrecked on one of the islands. Don't forget you haven't heard from him for ever so long. But of course, she comforted herself, that was the key to the mystery. She didn't know, she had no idea as to his movements. He could be ill, although it was difficult to imagine such a thing. Not Rick, with his deceptively wiry frame and lean strength.

All right then, something else? There could be a hundred reasons for the delay.

Including Craig's supposition, piped up a small devil deep in her mind. Another woman? Oh, not that Craig had said so in so many words, but the suggestion was there in the ironic look in his eyes. She pushed the absurd thought aside. Not Rick! He loved her too much!

That was the one bright spot in this endless time of waiting. That Craig hadn't been here to witness her disappointment. Oh, he'd have revelled in that. Nothing would have given him greater pleasure.

Thinking of Craig made her so angry that she blinked away the moisture that misted her eyes and took herself in hand. After all, there was always tomorrow, and the next day and the day after that. She had been an idiot to jump to dismal conclusions merely because Rick happened to be a few hours late for his appointment with her on the island. It was odd though. He would surely have let her know of the delay if he could. There must be a reason.

Well, she decided, she would wait here until the end of the week. After that . . . Her mind seemed to go blank. One thing was for sure, she couldn't afford to continue living in these luxurious surroundings. By diligent saving she had scraped enough money to cover the air fare, and luckily she had paid in advance to the travel agency for a week's stay at the hotel. She couldn't shake off the feeling that Rick would join her before long. All she had to do was to be patient. It was as simple as that.

Somehow, though, things didn't work out that way. The slow days dragged by and still there was no word from Rick, only the long hours of waiting.

On the last day of her stay at the Rarotongan Hotel she came to a decision. With the small amount of money left in her purse she would hire a bicycle, motor scooters were beyond her means, and she would visit the wharves in search of information about Rick. Why hadn't she explored that avenue earlier? Her spirits rose on a wave of hope. Who knows? Maybe she might even see the *Joanne* with its windfilled scarlet spinnaker sailing into Avarua harbour. Or failing that at least she might glean some word of the island-hopping craft.

Strange, she thought as she cycled out of the entrance on the hired bicycle, that she had been in this beautiful unspoilt island all week yet she hadn't yet been out of the hotel grounds. Now, as she took the winding road that followed the coast around the island, she could see the shadowy blue peaks of bush-covered mountains in the interior. There was little traffic, mainly motor scooters and bicycles and cars and trucks encrusted with rust.

As she pedalled along the quiet road the soft clear air was a delight. She passed timber houses, a weathered white church with spacious green lawns. Bananas and paw-paw grew wild at the roadside, avocados and mangoes were plentiful, and always the tall coconut palms moved softly in the breeze. If only Rick had been here with her. Swiftly she rallied her spirits. She wasn't giving up hope of meeting up with him yet. This could be her lucky day!

When she reached the harbour with its concrete breakwater she could see at once that there was no yacht in view. Only a weathered fishing trawler, a trim white schooner rocking at anchor and a rusted old cargo vessel loading copra at the wharf.

She propped the cycle against the sea wall and, dropping down on the springy green grass, she let the fresh, salty wind cool her hot cheeks. After a while she strolled along the road with its scattering of native stores, the verandas hung with gaudy cotton garments, strings of shell necklaces and baskets and sun hats decorated with violets and red poppies. In the open-air market, island women were seated beside their woven baskets overflowing with tropical fruits and green vegetables plucked only a few hours earlier. There was a modern trading-store, a few business offices, but Joanne's attention was caught by a small seafood café, its worn timbers decorated with murals of fish and seashells.

Pushing her way through the strips of plastic in the entrance, she made her way into the dim interior. No doubt seafaring men and crews of local fishing craft would eat here, she hazarded.

She dropped down to a table by a window overlooking the waters of the harbour and presently a young Rarotongan man with the friendly manner of his race approached her table. 'What would you like to order?'

Joanne studied the menu he had handed her, then selected a fish meal. 'Tell me,' she looked up at him, 'you must get to know a lot of seafaring guys. Sailors, fishermen and so on——'

He nodded. 'Oh, yes, when the boats come in.'

'Look,' she appealed to him, a sudden urgency in her tone, 'did you ever happen to come across a skipper of a white yacht with a scarlet spinnaker? The *Joanne* it's called.'

At his look of perplexity her heart sank.

'It might have been a while ago,' she persisted. 'I don't know exactly. Rick was the skipper's name, Rick Mason. He's cruising around the islands of the Pacific. I just thought——' At his puzzled expression her voice trailed into silence.

'I'm sorry.' He turned away.

She flicked a glance towards the only other diner in the room, a rugged-looking man of late middle age who was seated at a table opposite to her. Swiftly she took in his dark blue clothing and peaked cap, the cigarette smoke curling up from his weather-roughened face. Should she approach him? Why not? She had nothing to lose.

'Excuse me,' she raised her voice, 'could I ask you something?

'Sure.' He was stubbing out his cigarette in a clam

shell that served for an ashtray. Joanne thought he had a good-natured looking face. 'Fire away.'

'It's just——' She slipped from her seat and came to drop down in the chair opposite him. 'You're a seaman, I take it?' She was unaware of the desperate appeal in her blue eyes. 'Fisherman maybe? I'm only guessing.'

He grinned companionably. 'You got it right the first time. I'm on one of the boats trading around the islands. Once in a while we do the round trip. Auckland, Fiji, then on to the Cook Islands to pick up a load of copra and pearl-shell. All that sort of stuff.'

All at once her eyes were shining. 'But that's fantastic!'

'You reckon?' His lips twisted in a sceptical grin. 'Just a job.'

'No, no, that's not what I meant!' Her face was alight with excitement. 'You see,' she ran on in a rush of words, 'I'm trying to locate my friend. He's been sailing around the Pacific islands. You may have heard of him, Rick Mason.' She held her breath for the answer.

'Can't say that I have, miss.'

'Maybe you'd know his yacht, the *Joanne*. He promised to meet me here at Rarotonga. It was to be the last lap of his island cruise before he sailed back to New Zealand.'

'Afraid I can't help you with that one either.'

'I see.' She battled with the tide of bitter disappointment that was flooding over her. 'I was just . . . wondering.' After a moment she ran on, speaking her thoughts aloud. '*Something* must have happened to stop him being here to meet me on the day we planned. I only hope——' She was biting her thumbnail worriedly.

Something of her despairing thoughts must have got through to him for his eyes held an unexpected gentleness. 'Now don't you worry your head about your friend losing his craft in these waters or getting it holed or smashed up on one of the coral reefs, if that's what's on your mind.'

She swallowed the lump that had lodged itself in her throat. 'How did you guess?' It was a relief to unburden her fears to this kindly stranger. 'Storms too,' her eyes were anxious, 'supposing he had to abandon ship in bad weather?'

'Put it out of your mind.' His grin was reassuring. 'News travels mighty quick around the Pacific island ports and you'd have had word about a missing lone sailor long before this if he had struck that sort of trouble.'

She said on a sigh, 'That's what I try to tell myself.'

'Hold on a minute!' Suddenly his gaze sharpened. 'He wouldn't be a lanky young guy, this Rick character? Skinny bloke, sandy-coloured hair, quiet spoken?'

'Yes, Oh, *yes!*' She could scarcely contain her excitement. 'That's him! That's Rick! Tell me,' she leaned towards him eagerly, 'where did you see him?'

'Right here in Rarotonga! Ran into a guy in one of the bars here one night, can't for the life of me think which one.' His eyes twinkled. 'They all look the same to me after I've downed a few drinks.'

Joanne was holding her breath. 'Tell me.'

'Nothing much to tell. I was due to ship out of Rarotonga that night and we shared a couple of beers. I can't recall much about the guy. He wasn't much of a talker.'

'But he must have told you something about his plans,' she persisted. 'Please, *please* try to remember. Where he came from, what he was doing here, where he was going. Didn't he say anything about himself?'

Thoughtfully he scratched a grizzled head. 'Not much.'

'When was all this?'

'Let me see. Must have been on my last trip over this way. Say a couple of months.'

'Months!' The sense of let-down struck her like a blow, but she tried to pull her thoughts together. 'If you could just remember anything he said to you.' Her eyes, clear as a child's, swept up imploringly to his weather-lined face. 'Especially, did he say anything about coming back here later in the year?'

His eyes narrowed, sun wrinkles fanning at the corners in his effort at concentration. Then all at once his expression lightened. 'That rings a bell. Come to think of it, he did say something about having to wait here until the new spinnaker he'd ordered for his yacht arrived by Air N.Z. plane the next day. "See you around," he said, and something about there being a chance of his coming back here a bit later on if things turned out the way he hoped they would.'

'He said,' Joanne's face was flooded with relief, 'that he'd be back here again?' She had taken in only part of what the seaman had told her.

'It's not much to go on.'

'Oh but it is to me!' Her warm smile flashed out. 'Thank you for telling me.'

A grin creased his rugged features. 'Any time. Look.' All at once she realised he was regarding her thoughtfully. 'You don't think——' At her stormy expression he broke off.

She turned on him angrily. 'No! I don't think he's done a disappearing act just to avoid me, if that's what you're getting at!'

He waved the suggestion aside. 'Nothing further from my mind.' But she knew he was only trying to placate her.

'I'm sorry,' she muttered. She had lost her temper, she

realised now, because lying at the back of her consciousness was the unwelcome possibility to which she had
refused to give credence. It was Craig who had put the
idea in her mind. He was the one at whom her anger was
really directed. And she had vented her ill temper on this
stranger who had tried to help her.

'Forget it.' His eyes, surrounded by sun-wrinkles,
were kindly. 'Don't worry about your boyfriend. He'll
catch up with you sooner or later.'

'Of course he will!' Her smile had a sudden radiance.
'And thanks again. You've been ever so helpful.'

He found himself wishing it were the truth. There
was something about the girl that put him in mind of his
own twenty-year-old daughter. The same mop of black
curls and air of vitality as if she couldn't wait to get on
with life! Thoughtfully he lighted another cigarette and
watched the blue smoke curl upwards. Guy she thought
so much of had probably forgotten all about her, got
himself another woman by now. His face darkened. He
knew how he'd feel if some foot-loose yachtie let his own
daughter down like that!

'Your order, miss.' The café proprietor placed a plate
down at her table. 'I caught that fish early this morning
and cooked it myself.'

'Great!' She smiled up at him but she scarcely tasted
the appetising meal he had brought her. Her thoughts
were whirling. Now at last she had something to go on.
No one else but Rick could have fitted the stranger's
description so well. And Rick had spoken of his return
to the island. It was just as she had suspected. He'd been
delayed, but any day now he'd be sailing into the
harbour. Yet a sense of unease plucked at her mind.
Why had Rick come here earlier than he had planned
and left again? But of course she thrust the worrying
thoughts aside, there would be a simple explanation for

his change of plan. He would have explained it all to her in a letter, the letter she had never received from him. All that mattered was that he would be coming back to Rarotonga. She had only to stick around here until he arrived.

Stay on here at the island? Without money? Without friends? And it wasn't as if anyone back home in New Zealand could lend her sufficient funds to carry on for a while. She had only one option.

The thought she had pushed to the back of her mind surfaced. You know what you have to do, don't you? came the calm voice of reason. You've got to ask that hateful Craig to help you out.

I can't! I just can't! I loathe the man!

What's that got to do with it? Think of Rick. If you love him——

Of course I love him.

There was only one course of action open to her and she'd known it all along, only she hadn't faced up to it. Now she knew she had no choice. I'll go and see him today, she decided firmly, get it over with while I've got my courage screwed up sufficiently to tackle him.

At the counter she paid for her meal then enquired of the young proprietor directions on how to get to the Kia Orana Motel.

'The new one that's going up? Run by a New Zealand guy?'

'That's the one.'

'It's quite a way from here, on the other side of the island. Do you have transport?'

She nodded. 'Sort of.'

'Follow the main road around the island,' he told her. 'Past the perfume factory you'll see a big white church. The Kia Orana is down the side road. The units aren't open for business yet, I'm told,' he volunteered. 'Should be ready very soon, though. A bit early for calling in if you're a tourist wanting to be put up, but the right time for anyone wanting a job there.'

She smiled across at him. 'It's an idea. Thanks a lot.'

'Good luck!' called the seaman as she passed by his table on the way out of the café. His eyes were sympathetic.

'Thank you.' Why did everyone persist in feeling sorry for her? she asked herself resentfully. She knew Rick would be here to meet her. He had been delayed for a while, that was all.

At the entrance she paused, dazzled by the brilliant sunshine after the dimness of the café. If only she didn't have to approach *him*. But there was no one else she could call on, and he had offered to help her should she need assistance. Squaring her shoulders, she set her lips determinedly then moved towards the cycle propped against the sea wall. 'Come along you, on your way!' She wheeled the bike out to the main road and soon she was pedalling along beside the harbour, a small figure on a large bike, bumping over potholes and stones on the dirt road, her dark hair flying behind her ears in the sea breeze.

All the way along the rough thoroughfare she wrestled with her decision. The closer she came to her destination, the more she was tempted to abandon the idea. There must be some other way out of her dilemma if only she could think of it. Anything would be preferable to asking help of Craig—Craig of all men!

All at once she became aware of someone waving to her from a passing car and as the vehicle slowed to a stop beside her she recognised a honeymoon couple from the hotel. 'We're making the most of our last day here, yours too?' called a girl's voice.

'I'm staying on a bit longer.'

'Lucky you!' The car slid forward.

Lucky! Joanne was hot and flushed as she pedalled on. She tried to tell herself that, with hair plastered to her forehead with beads of perspiration, she needed to slow down her energetic pushing on the bike pedals. But deep down she knew she was slowing speed because the last thing in the world she wanted to do was to arrive at her destination.

All too soon a white-painted timber church loomed into view and soon she caught sight of a signpost half hidden among trees. 'Kia Orana Motel'. An arrow pointed towards a side street. *Kia Orana,* Welcome to our Island. Craig extending a welcome to *her* at his motel! The thought was beyond the bounds of possibility. She had half a mind to turn back. There must be some other way out of her difficulties. She simply couldn't approach him for help. But she must.

Suddenly she was at the corner of the road and she steeled herself to go on. Absorbed in her thoughts, she didn't see the Alsatian dog running across the roadway directly in her path until it was too late. She slewed violently to avoid the animal and in that split second she became aware of a red car that was almost upon her. A horrendous crash, then the world spun around her to splinter into fragments, and then she was plunging down, down, into an intense darkness shot with flashing red lights.

CHAPTER FOUR

JOANNE must have lost consciousness for a few seconds, for the next thing of which she was aware was a sensation of being gathered up in strong arms. Masculine tones that seemed vaguely familiar to her echoed in her ears.

'What the hell do you think you're doing, charging around without looking where you're going?'

Her dazed vision cleared and she looked up into Craig's face. The odd thing was that he was shouting at her, furious with her, judging by his tone, she thought dreamily, yet his eyes looked distraught.

'You're OK?' His low tone was husky with emotion. 'Tell me, you're not hurt, Joanne?' The words came on a sharp breath and his eyes were dark and anxious.

Slowly she gathered her scattered wits together. She pushed the cluster of curls from her eyes, and then, as if looking at someone else, she eyed the smears of dust and blood on her arm. Curiously she rubbed away the dirt to reveal a long scratch. 'It's nothing,' she murmured. 'I'm all right.' She gave a wavering smile. 'Truly I am. There's nothing to worry about.'

'I only hope you're right.' His voice was grim, and she realised he was eyeing her intently, the distraught note still in his tone.

He put her down gently in his car and slowly she fitted the pieces of the puzzle together. He must have carried her here after—'The bike!' Her gaze went to the twisted pieces of metal lying in the dust of the roadway. Now it was her own eyes that were wide with alarm, her voice tense and anxious. 'It's all twisted up,' she whispered. 'It's a wreck. Whatever will it cost to have it repaired?'

'Not a thing! I'll take care of it—or the insurance company will! Forget it,' he said carelessly, 'it wasn't much to start with by the look of it.'

'But——'

'Come on, I'll get you back to the motel and make sure there's no damage done.'

'Damage? The bike, you mean?' She raised dazed blue eyes, wide with alarm.

'Not the bike, dammit!' She couldn't believe that Craig, so self-possessed, so bitingly calm, could be shouting at her in this way. 'It's *you*, Joanne! You should take better care of yourself!'

That sounded more like the Craig she knew, she thought dreamily. Taking her to task, blaming her for everything.

She murmured, 'Do you always drive this way?'

'What do you mean?'

'So slowly. That dog on the other side of the road is trotting along faster than we are.'

'For Pete's sake!' He was shouting at her once again. 'Don't you understand? You took a crack on the head just now, enough to put you out for a bit. It could be serious. On this road you could be jolted to pieces if I didn't take it carefully.'

'Oh!' She relaxed on the seat, pondering the matter. There was something about Craig she couldn't understand. He was acting as though she were someone of great import to him, a girl to be considered, protected, taken care of. Then the penny dropped and realisation came back with a rush. Could

it be that the accident hadn't been entirely her fault?
Had he taken the tree-shrouded corner too sharply,
too fast, been driving carelessly? That would explain
why he seemed so anxious to make certain she wasn't
seriously injured. He had no wish to take
responsibility for a girl who had been hurt in an
accident involving himself.

'Here we are!'

A name carved on a stone at the entrance had to
Joanne a familiar ring. 'Kia Orana'. She had been
going there anyway, to see him about something . . .
something important. The reason for the visit eluded
her but it didn't matter anyway. It would come back
to her before long.

They were turning in at the foot of a slope, taking a
newly formed pathway winding up a rise. Two island
boys were working on the grassy slope planting
shrubs and digging holes. As the car neared the top of
the rise she could see men painting a long low
building and near by she glimpsed a series of units
built of dark brown timbers and stepped so that each
was a separate unit with a view of the lagoon.

Involuntarily she said, 'It's all just like the plan you
were showing me that night on the plane.'

'Great!' He sent her a quick glance and all at once
the tense lines of his face relaxed. 'You remember
that?'

She said slowly, 'It's all coming back.' Oh yes, it
was coming back only too clearly, she mused on a
sigh. Right at this moment she didn't know how she
was going to get through the ordeal that lay ahead.
Unconsciously she twisted a tendril of hair round and
round her finger. Bad enough for her and Craig to
have this irrational antipathy to each other. Now she
had caused him to have an accident with his car,

albeit a minor one. If only the dog hadn't run across the road in front of her, made her swerve into his vehicle.

She bit her lip thoughtfully and of course his perceptive glance took in her worried expression. 'How are you feeling? Got a headache?'

She shook her head. 'It's nothing much.' How could she explain to him that her headache, she was sure, stemmed from this meeting with him?

He had braked the car to a stop outside a door with the word 'Office' written on a board. The next moment he was out of the car and opening the passenger door for her, extending a hand to help her out of the vehicle.

'It's all right,' she said stiffly. 'I can manage fine now.'

He eyed her doubtfully. 'Are you sure?'

As she stepped down to the pathway a wave of dizziness swept her but it was gone in a moment. He led her into a room with rattan blinds, a long counter and pigeon-holes for mail, files, and a desk, a typewriter.

'Take a seat.' He pulled forward a cane chair and she sank down.

'Can I get you a drink? It's not a bad idea right now.' He had moved towards a cocktail cabinet. 'A gin, sherry——?'

'Just a fruit drink, please.'

'Right. Take your pick. There's mango, pineapple, passion fruit.'

'Anything that's cool.'

'Coming right up!' Ice tinkled in the glass, then he handed her a drink of mango. Joanne sipped it slowly, her mind busy with the ordeal that lay ahead.

'Let's take a look at that scratch on your arm.' He

was bending towards her, wiping away the dust and blood, then applying disinfectant and a bandage.

'How does it feel?' He stood looking down at her, his eyes dark with concern.

'Much better.' But she scarcely knew what she was saying. She was unprepared for the reaction his touch on her skin evoked, the raw force of his male attraction.

Somehow she fought herself free of the wild confusion of her senses, made herself concentrate on the object of this visit to Craig. She supposed she owed him an explanation of some sort for what had happened out there on the road. 'It was the Alsatian dog,' she murmured slowly, 'it ran right in front of me. I tried to avoid it but it was too late. Honestly, I didn't even see it coming!'

His perceptive gaze slid over her petite figure. 'There doesn't seem to be any serious damage done. That's all that matters.'

'I keep telling you,' she said with spirit, 'there's nothing wrong with me.'

'All right, all right, I believe you!'

This was the moment she had been dreading. She stared down into her empty glass. 'Actually I was on my way here.'

'I know.' He had a way of looking her straight in the eye. 'I've been expecting you.'

Suddenly she was alert. 'What's that supposed to mean?'

He shrugged broad shoulders. 'Just that I happen to know you've been at the Rarotongan Hotel all week on your own. I did tell you to contact me if you got into any sort of difficulty.'

She said, very low, 'Yes, I know you did, but——'

'You didn't want to do that?' He shot the words at

her like bullets. 'Why not?'

She avoided his piercing gaze. 'I just—didn't want to.'

He was standing looking down at her, tall, implacable and, the traitorous thought came unbidden, heart-knockingly attractive. Just the sight of him was sending her carefully rehearsed speech flying from her mind.

'So,' he went on. She brought her mind back to his resonant tones. 'I take it you've run out of cash. Got enough funds to settle your hotel bill?'

'Oh, yes, that was paid before I left New Zealand. It's just——' She looked up at him with clear blue eyes. 'I know that Rick will turn up before long. It's just a matter of waiting.'

'I get it.' He was drawing a wallet from the pocket of his faded blue denim jeans. 'You want a loan to carry you on for a while. Just say how much you need.'

'No, it's not like that! You don't understand!' she lashed out at him. 'I've got to get a job!' She drew a deep breath. He could only refuse her request. 'I thought,' she hurried on, 'that, seeing you're just about to open your restaurant here, maybe you could give me some work.'

'Such as?' His cool enquiring tone was anything but encouraging to her taut nerves.

'Cooking! I am qualified for working as a chef,' she went on before he could turn her down. 'I've had the training in New Zealand and I've got my diploma—cordon bleu—to prove it!'

His voice was dangerously quiet. 'But no practical experience in a hotel or restaurant, so you told me.' Damn him, she thought bitterly, he would remember our conversation on this subject on the flight here. 'I don't know about that,' his eyes had a veiled expression, 'it's a tall order.'

'Oh, I know you've got someone else lined up for the job,' she ran on, 'but I just thought—I mean, there's no harm in asking!' She hated being forced to plead with him in this way. Go on, she ordered herself, *ask him*. A thought crossed her mind. 'And I know the Maori language, well, near enough. I had to study it for schoolteaching and it's very close to the Rarotongan one.'

He waved the suggestion aside.

'No need for that. The staff I've engaged to work at Kia Orana speak English as fluently as they do their own language.'

'But you wouldn't be sorry if you took me on!' Unconsciously her small tanned hands were clasped tightly together. 'Honestly, I could cope with the work, serving food grown on the island and all.' He made no answer, and she said in a low tone, 'I wouldn't let you down.'

'Wouldn't you?' The glint in his eyes mocked her. 'And how about if your Rick turned up here next week? What then?'

'It wouldn't make any difference.' Dizzy with sudden hope, she would have promised him anything, anything. 'If I were working for you I'd stay on. Rick would have his boat and I'd have some spare time when we could be together. Truly,' her low tones held a desperate entreaty, 'you wouldn't be sorry if you took me on. I've just *got* to have a job! Do you think——' The words died away for, glancing up at him, she saw that his eyes had the cold glint of steel. It was hopeless for her even to think that he might go out of his way to help her out of her difficulty. She must have been out of her mind to approach him in the matter.

Throwing common sense to the winds rustling the tall coconut palms outside the window she said very low, 'I might have known it would be no use asking you.'

She knew she had really blown her chances of a job with him. He would never offer her the work now and she would rather die than accept his offer of a loan of money.

'OK then,' his words took her by surprise, 'we'll give it a trial run for three months. How does that grab you?'

She opened her lips to speak, then closed them again. 'But your friend back in New Zealand, the one who's a chef at an Auckland restaurant?'

'I'll square things with him. He isn't all that keen on island living.'

'And I can have the job?' She still couldn't take it in.

'Subject to your delivering the goods!' His cool, matter-of-fact tones brought her down to earth with a bump. 'A set-up like this one depends a lot on a first-class restaurant.' All at once his eyes were pale and distant. 'It's a chance I've got to take.' Ice tinkled in his tones. 'Now it's up to you. I only hope——'

He broke off and she knew only too well the words he had left unsaid: 'That you don't ruin the reputation of the motel before it gets off the ground.'

'You don't sound very enthusiastic about taking me on!' The words were past her lips before she could stop to think.

'As I said,' came his inflexible tones, 'it's a trial run. Usual rates of pay, days off by mutual arrangement. Starting in two days' time—that suit you?'

As if he didn't know that she had no option in the

matter. 'You don't need to pretend,' she said huffily. 'I don't have any choice, do I?'

He bent on her his implacable stare. 'You said you wanted the job.'

'Oh, I do, I do!' Common sense told her that she was acting unreasonably. 'It's all right,' she said in a milder tone, 'you won't be sorry about taking me on,' and she made a mental vow that she would make a success of this venture, no matter what!

'Right. That's settled then. I'll get you to put your signature to a contract later.' He appeared to dismiss the matter of her employment from his mind. He turned on her one of his penetrating glances. 'How are you feeling?'

'I'm fine now—there's just one thing——'

Immediately his voice was sharp with concern. 'I can get a doctor right away. Just tell me——'

'No, no, nothing like that! There's nothing wrong with me. It's the bike.'

'The *bike?*' His tone was incredulous. 'You mean that heap of old metal back on the road?'

She ignored that comment. 'It's just, could you take it back to the hotel for me? I only hired it for a day. Tell them I had a bit of a crash-up but I'll fix up any charges for damages,' she drew a deep breath, 'before long.'

'Will do.'

'Oh, and while you're there could you bring my travel bag back with you? One of the housemaids will throw any of my things that are lying around the room into it. If I'm going to stay on here——'

'Just what I had in mind. If you're quite sure,' he was eyeing her closely, 'that you'll be all right here on your own until I get back.'

She laughed away the query. 'Of course I'll be all

right.'

'I'll get cracking then.'

He was turning away when she called after him. 'Just one other thing', and she ran on quickly before he could argue the matter, 'Would you pick up mail for me at the reception desk?'

'If there is any!' She flinched at the contempt in his voice. 'You sure are a devil for punishment!'

She could have wrung his neck. 'And you never believe a word I tell you!' she flung after him. 'Even when it's the truth! One of these days you'll find you've been all wrong about Rick's not turning up here to meet me, you'll see.'

He had reached the door and his cool tones floated back to her. 'I can hardly wait!'

Suddenly he swung around and took a few steps towards her. 'You'll take it easy while I'm away? I won't be long.' All at once his eyes were dark with concern. 'You'll rest for a bit?'

She nodded, but she had no intention of doing as he suggested, *ordered* rather! Apart from a slight sensation of dizziness, she was feeling perfectly well.

Look on the bright side, she told herself. Think positively and wonderful things can happen! She hadn't been hurt in the accident, even although her *pareu* was torn beyond repair. Her damaged cycle was being taken care of, and, most important of all, she had got herself work that would support her until Rick's arrival on the island.

If you can make a go of the job to Craig's satisfaction, a small devil whispered deep in her mind. But she thrust it aside. She was determined to make a success of the opportunity he had offered her, albeit reluctantly. Even though she had a suspicion that the man who had light-heartedly partnered her in an island

dance might well prove to be an exacting employer
who demanded the highest possible standards from
his staff.

The moment that Craig's red car was out of sight on
the winding driveway she slipped out of the door and
made her way along a path lined with frangipani
bushes. Soon she had reached a sprawling dark timber
building that was the restaurant Craig had told her
about.

Curious to find out the amenities of the kitchen that
was to be her workplace for the next few months she
tried the door but found it locked. Moving to a
window, she raised herself on tiptoe to peer inside.

If he had the nerve to expect her to toil in a hot
kitchen under primitive conditions in the heat—but
she need not have worried, she told herself the next
moment. For the spacious room was lined with
gleaming stainless steel benches and storage units and
fitted with the latest labour-saving appliances. Best of
all were the huge fans that were fitted to the ceiling.
Thank heaven for that!

Presently she was strolling over the golden sands
where plastic seats were stacked, then she moved to a
small building obviously intended for use as a beach
centre, where snorkels and all manner of beach
equipment could be hired.

Passing a stack of kayaks, she paused to pick up a
plastic surf-board with a viewing-glass at one end. She
promised herself that she would try out the board at
the first opportunity. It would be fun to peer down at
the jewel-like tropical fish as they moved in the waters
out by the reef.

There was no doubt, she mused, that for tourists
staying at the Kia Orana the setting was most
attractive. All at once Craig's words echoed in her

mind and she felt a moment's trepidation. Hadn't he
told her that the real test for a pleasure-seeking tourist
on the island lay in the high quality of food served at
the restaurant of a motel?

He was placing an awful lot of trust in her
capabilities, that was for sure, but he wouldn't regret
having offered her the job. Hateful, autocratic,
interfering he might be, but she wouldn't let him
down.

A blaze of rose and gold fanned over the western sky
as Craig pulled up his car in the driveway beside
Joanne.

He stepped down at her side and without warning a
surge of pleasure washed over her. And wouldn't you
know it, his pale steely gaze hadn't missed her
expression.

He said quizzically, 'You're looking mighty pleased
to see me.' The glint in his eyes mocked her. 'Makes a
nice change.'

Hurriedly she rearranged her expression. 'Oh, I am
glad to see you! I'm hoping there was a letter waiting
for me at the hotel.'

'No mail for you.' He lifted her travel bag from the
car and set it down on the palm-shaded pathway.

'A message for me, maybe?'

He shrugged broad shoulders. 'I didn't enquire.'

'No, you wouldn't!' The familiar feeling of
frustration and tension came rushing back and she
was angry with him all over again. 'You don't believe
me, do you?' she burst out. 'You think I'm crazy to
stay on here, just waiting.'

'Up to you.' His tone was taut with suppressed
anger. A sardonic smile curved his lips. 'It's good to
see you're back in fighting form!' All at once his

expression softened. 'You're OK now? That's all I care about.'

She eyed him suspiciously, but he actually appeared to mean what he said. But of course. Why must she keep forgetting the real motive underlying his concern for her health?

'I'm feeling on top of the world!' she assured him, and strangely all at once it was the truth. 'And I know why!' She looked up at him challengingly. 'I've got news for you! Guess what happened today? I found out something about Rick.'

'You *what?*' At last, she thought triumphantly, she had cracked his cool composure.

'It's true,' she ran on in a flurry of words. 'I was down on the wharves,' her eyes glowed at the thought, 'and would you believe it? I happened to run into a man in a café there who'd been speaking to Rick, right here in this town.'

At the satirical look in his eyes she burst out defensively, 'So it just goes to show that Rick *was* here. The seaman told me.'

'Just when was this meeting?' His cool staccato tones cut across her excited accents.

'When?' The question sent her chin tilting upwards. 'Two months ago. But at least it's something. I know now that he'll be coming back here to meet me as we arranged. He's just been delayed a little, that's all.'

His all-too-perceptive pale eyes seemed to be boring into 'Did the seaman know Rick by name?'

'Well, no.' Swiftly she ran on before he could make one of his sarcastic comments. 'But it was Rick whom he met. I know it was. The way the man described him it couldn't have been anyone else. It just couldn't!' To her horror she heard the wobble in her voice. She hurried on breathlessly. 'It seems Rick was here for a couple of days waiting for a new spinnaker to arrive by plane from New Zealand. And do you know what?' She had kept the best part of her news until the last. 'Rick told the seaman that he'd be coming back here before long. I know what that meant.'

'You do?'

She threw him an angry look. Oh, he was determined to be obstinate in the matter. She might have known he wouldn't believe that Rick intended to return here.

His voice sharpened. 'Did the guy you spoke to know Rick's yacht, the *Joanne?*'

'Not really, but——'

His dark eyebrows climbed. 'So all you have to pin your hopes on is a few words from someone you met up with in a café. If you want my opinion——'

She threw him a tight-lipped glance. 'I don't.'

The relentless tones swept on unheedingly. 'A man you happened to run into down on the wharves.' His well shaped lips curled scornfully. 'How do you know he wasn't stringing you a line? Leading you on? Saying what you wanted him to say? Because of the way you were looking at him?' For a second tiny lights glowed deep in his eyes. 'A girl like you. How do you know he wasn't just chatting you up?'

'You don't understand,' she blazed defensively, 'he wasn't like that! If you'd talked with him yourself——'

'If I had,' he cut in grimly, 'I'd have wanted a lot more information than something about a guy he'd met for a few minutes, when was it? Months ago!'

'He was only trying to help,' she persisted stubbornly. 'If you'd been there you'd have known.'

'True,' he agreed with irony.

She squared her shoulders, took a deep breath and tried to keep control of her temper. Somehow she wasn't having much success in that field. 'It *was* Rick who the man met at the tavern a while ago. I know it was!' All at once her stormy expression cleared. 'I know what I'll do,' she declared on an impulse. 'I'll take a trip around the taverns here and see if I can't find out something about Rick from someone else who may have met him!' She warmed to the idea. 'I'll go tonight and I'll call in at every nightspot on the island!'

Suddenly he was tense and alert. 'No!' The word came explosively.

She glared at him defiantly, her eyes shooting sparks. 'I will, you know! If you think I'm going to miss a chance, any chance, of getting a line on Rick's movements while he was here——' She broke off, eyeing him steadily. 'I'll be quite all right, you know, if that's what's on your mind. You needn't worry about me.' As if he would. 'I'll be perfectly safe. Everyone says that here on the island there's no need to——'

'Oh, it's safe enough.'

She eyed him resentfully. 'Well then, why on earth are you making such a—a thing of a little trip around the nightspots?'

'You took a tumble off the bike today, remember?'

'Oh, that,' she scoffed, 'it was nothing.'

'Enough to put you out for a while.' He stood regarding her, lean and tall and implacable, one thumb hooked in the low-slung belt of his jeans. 'You're not going it alone.'

'I keep telling you,' she declared with elaborate patience, 'I'm feeling fine now.' Her warm smile flashed out. 'And rarin' to go!' She threw him a defiant glance. 'And I don't need an escort tonight thank you very much!'

As they stepped into the office the shrill peal of the telephone bell rang through the room. After a short conversation Craig replaced the receiver in its cradle. He turned to eye her quizzically. 'The bad news is that the restaurant opening is off for another week, some hitch in the plumbing department. The good news is for you.'

'For me?' She stared at him bewilderedly.

He nodded. 'You can take a week off duty. It will give you a chance to make those "missing person" enquiries you're so anxious about.'

She eyed him in disbelief. 'But I thought you didn't believe that Rick was coming back—ever?'

His pale eyes were unreadable. 'That's right.'

'Yet you'd let me have a week off work on full pay?' she said incredulously. Surprise and pleasure rang in her tone. 'You'd really do that for me?'

'For me, actually'. She had a feeling of cold water being dashed in her face. 'I can't afford to employ a chef who can't keep her mind on her work. If you turn up anything on your missing yachtsman you might be able to relax a bit.'

'Thanks very much!' She spoke through gritted teeth. She was so mad with him she could have flung something at his head, preferably a hard, hurtful object like one of the coconuts hanging high on the palm tree outside the window.

'Joanne,' his voice was low and controlled, 'there's something——'.

Instantly she was on the defensive. Her lips tightened. 'If you're trying to put me off taking a look around the taverns tonight——'

The look in his eyes was unfathomable. 'Look, I'll

hand it to you straight.'

'What's that supposed to mean?' She eyed him defiantly.

'Just, well, has it ever crossed your mind that your precious Rick might not be all that pleased with the notion of your hanging around the island week after week waiting for him to put in an appearance?'

Danger flags flew in her cheeks. 'No, it hasn't! I don't know what you're getting at.'

'Oh, yes, you do. Ask yourself.' There was a wicked glint in his eyes. 'Remember my Uncle Joshua?'

'Oh, shut up about your Uncle Joshua!' she snapped. 'He sounds like a lecherous old man to me.'

'My own age exactly,' came Craig's smooth tones, 'when he made the big break of his life and came back to Rarotonga to marry his island sweetheart.'

'I don't see,' she flung at him angrily, 'what all that has to do with me! I don't know what you're getting at but if it's what I think it is——'

His cool stare mocked her. 'Just a thought.'

She managed a scornful laugh. 'If you knew Rick——'

'Are you sure that you do?'

'Of course I'm sure! He's just not that sort of man. Even if,' she swallowed the lump that had lodged itself in her throat, 'he did want—if he'd changed his mind about me, about us, he'd come right out with it. He wouldn't just do a disappearing act into the blue Pacific.'

'Maybe he did write you about something that was important to him. One of those letters that didn't get through to you. After all, it happens.'

'Anyway, what matters to me is that he could be ill and alone or hurt in some way. Anything could have happened to him.'

'Exactly,' came Craig's maddening tones, 'just what I'm trying to tell you.'

'I know what you're trying to tell me,' she said tightly, 'and it's got nothing to do with Rick and me. Couples aren't like that nowadays, they act differently. Men and women who have a caring relationship trust each other. They don't go around the world playing sneaky tricks on someone they love.'

He sent her one of those sceptical glances he seemed to keep just for her and any mention of Rick.

'Who do you think you are?' She faced him angrily with flushed cheeks. 'Handing out advice to me about Rick. You've never seen him. Do you fancy yourself as some sort of marriage counsellor or something?'

'Just trying to help.' His lazy accents were infuriating to her taut nerves. 'Cushion the shock for you if there is one.'

'Well, there won't be anything like that.' She tossed her head defiantly. 'And even if I were in any trouble about Rick, you'd be the last one I'd come to for help.'

The thoughts ran wildly through her mind. Rick running away to a Pacific island, staying on there with a lovely native girl. It was so absurd she could smile at the idea. But she didn't feel like smiling, she was so angry with Craig. He seemed to take a fiendish delight in provoking her. She could hardly wait to prove to him how mistaken he was in his ridiculous assumption about Rick.

'About dinner tonight.' His voice broke across her angry musing and she could see by the taut line of his lips that she had at last got through to him.

With an effort she schooled her voice to a note of polite interest. After all, she supposed she did owe him something for the week off work. She said stiffly,

'I could fix a meal for us here.'

'No, you couldn't! The kitchen's a bit haywire right now but I'll be getting in supplies tomorrow. We'll get a bite to eat in town. If you're wondering about sleeping arrangements, I hang out in the first unit in the staff block.'

She held her breath, the thoughts milling wildly through her mind. If he had any ideas about expecting favours from her in return for his job offer . . . if he imagined . . .

'You can take your pick of the other apartments in the block.' Nothing could have been more impersonal than his tone.

She glanced at the units he had reserved for the staff at the motel. 'I'll settle for the end one,' she said crisply.

'Right! I'll take you down there.' They moved down the pathway then turned into the filtered light of a track winding among paw-paw trees and coconut and banana palms. When they reached the last of the units in the block of buildings he unlocked the door of the apartment and saw her into a tastefully furnished room with cool décor in shadings of beige and bamboo.

In the doorway he paused. 'You still want to go on that pub crawl?'

'Do I ever!'

'Feel up to it?'

'Of course I do!' Her eyes were bright with defiance. 'What's wrong with taking a look around the taverns? I think it's a terrific idea.'

His only answer was an enigmatic look. 'Here.' He tossed a key towards her. 'You'll be needing this. Pick you up at seven, OK?' He swung around and left her.

'Oh, I'll be ready long before then!' she called after

him. If he imagined, she thought hotly, that she intended to spend her time prettying herself up on his account tonight he was sadly mistaken.

With scarcely a glance around her luxurious surroundings, she unzipped her travel bag and began to toss undergarments and beachwear into drawers with careless abandon. Her mind was still seething with thoughts of Craig. The devil! How dared he talk to her that way! He took a fiendish delight in trying to shake her faith in Rick and his promise to meet her here on the island. If only Craig weren't her boss, well, near enough, she'd, she'd . . . She set her soft lips mutinously. But he was.

Some time later she took stock of her surroundings, the place that was to be her living-quarters for the next three months. Three long months! Her heart sank at the length of time she had let herself in for. Then with an effort she pulled her thoughts together. What were a few months when you were living on a tropical island with the man you loved?

The man you loved. Without warning there flashed on the screen of her mind a picture of Craig's attractive face and disturbing eyes. Now where in the world could that thought have come from? Swiftly she banished Craig's image from her mind. Small wonder she could think of no other man, for since her arrival on the island he seemed to have dominated her life—or tried to.

She had to admit that the unit, cool and spacious, with its long picture windows with a view of the reef, was well planned for comfort. Twin beds with bamboo-coloured spreads, a small table, an electric point and toaster, hot-water jug. She flipped open the door of a small fridge to find it well stocked with milk, wines, liqueurs and fruit drinks.

Then she wandered into the beautifully appointed bathroom with its gleaming bath and shower, long mirrors and cupboards stocked with fluffy towels.

Tonight she left her face entirely free of make-up and she was ready for the outing long before the ring of the doorbell shrilled through the room.

'Come in!' As she opened the door he glanced down at his wristwatch. His eyes held a mocking gleam. 'You're bang on time, even without your watch!'

So he had noticed her shattered gold watch after the accident today? Was there anything concerning her, she wondered, that he failed to take note of?

The next moment she warned herself it would be wiser not to gaze directly into his steely eyes. He was much too sure of himself, much too attractive in a lithe, tanned, masculine sort of way, especially tonight.

Wide-shouldered and slim-hipped, he moved with grace and distinction, the crisp, dark linen *pareu* tied around his waist swinging around his tanned ankles. He wore a cream-coloured short-sleeved shirt, his dark hair still damp from the shower, and she sensed an attraction about him so potent it was heart-stopping. And she loathed the man!

He said evenly, 'That *pareu* you're wearing is a bit of an advance on the one you had on when you crashed on the bike today!' His eyes said, 'You look wonderful!'

'Think so?' A wild, sweet excitement was taking possession of her senses and she felt as though she were drowning in his gaze, floundering in deep waters. Conscious of the eyes that never left her face, she heard her own voice saying thickly, happily, 'You like me in this?'

The next moment she could have bitten out her

tongue. The smash-up earlier in the day must have done something to her head. The moment of silence underlined her crashing blunder.

'Looks cooler,' he murmured off-handedly.

She could feel the pink creeping up her cheeks. Blushing! A habit she had thought to have left behind with vulnerable teenage years. What could have got into her to play right into his hands with that ill-chosen remark? All at once she hated him more fiercely than ever. Clearly, now that he had satisfied himself that she was unhurt after the collision with his car, he had gone right back to his real character. And she had best not forget it!

'Let's go, shall we?' He stood aside for her to leave the room, but instead she remained perfectly still.

'You don't have to take me out tonight——' She broke off abruptly, for there was something in his mocking glance that sent everything flying from her mind. At last she wrenched her gaze aside. 'I'm sure you must have oodles of more important things to do tonight than going on a pub crawl—with me.'

His eyes darkened formidably. 'I said I'd take you.'

And, taking in his closed expression, she knew that he meant business. 'Well,' she challenged him with spirit, 'I can't very well stop you!'

'Just you try!' She barely caught the low, gritted words.

CHAPTER FIVE

AS THEY moved out into the perfumed night Joanne paused to pluck a pink hibiscus blossom from a bush overhanging the pathway. Idly she lifted her hand to tuck the flower in her dark tresses.

'I hope you know what you're doing.' Craig's tones were threaded with amusement, and in the soft glow of the flares she caught his quirky smile.

'Just putting a flower in my hair. I thought,' she murmured airily, 'that I might as well look as if I belonged here.'

'So long as you beam out the right signal.' There was a cryptic note in his tones. 'Get the message across island-style.'

'Oh, yes,' for once she could meet him on his own ground, 'I'm all clued up about the flower-behind-the-ear significance.' She added smugly, 'One of the Rarotongan girls let me into it. Tuck it behind a girl's left ear, this way,' she avoided his ironic glance, 'and the message is "I already have a boyfriend".'

'In other words, "Get out!"'

'Well anyway, it says I'm married.'

'But you're not, are you?' he objected in the bland tone that she found so infuriating.

'I know! I know!' Wildly she sought in her mind for a suitable word. 'But I'm "bespoken", shall we say?'

'Oh, is that what you call it? The island girls say it all in a couple of words, "Go away!" And the flower worn on the other side of the head,' he pursued in his

78

deceptively soft tones, 'how about that?'

'Oh that's simple, it's——'

"Yes, please." There was a dancing glint in his eyes, 'They're very polite about these things, the islanders. There's another option to that one,' she didn't trust the amused note in his voice one little bit, 'or didn't the girl let you in on that one?'

Uncertain whether to believe him or not she shook her head. Before she could guess his intention he had raised his hand towards her and in a deft movement he flicked the blossom back from her face.

She said in surprise, 'What's that supposed to mean?'

'Oh, that's a special one if you read it right.'

'Meaning?'

Suddenly his voice was low and vibrant. 'Do not speak to me. Do not even look at me. But later——'

'Later?'

'I am yours—until dawn.'

There was something in his tone that sent the blood coursing wildly through her veins. With an effort she gathered her scattered senses together and with a hand that was suddenly unsteady she pushed the blossom back to its original position in her hair. 'There! That's plain enough! Says I'm just not interested!'

'I didn't think you would be.'

She eyed him suspiciously, but his expression was unreadable.

A short time later, seated at a table in the small restaurant to which Craig had taken her, she picked at the delectable meal on her plate. Absorbed in her thoughts, her hopes of the outcome of the evening ahead, she made no attempt at idle chatter. The maddening thing was, she told herself, that her com-

panion appeared not to notice her lack of polite
conversation, let alone the resentful glances she shot
at him across the table. Trust him to be enjoying his
meal immensely.

It was a delicious meal, she admitted to herself, yet
she had no appetite. Blame Craig for that. Her soft
lips set mutinously. Inviting himself to be her escort
for the trip around the taverns, dismissing as of no
importance her feelings in the matter.

Impatient to be on her way, Joanne felt as if the
meal would never come to an end, but at last they left
the table and stepped out into the island night. The
moon was a silver boat sailing the velvety darkness
and the stars were bright crystals one felt one could
almost reach up and touch. A night for love. The
thought ran through her mind. And here she was in
these romantic surroundings with the one man in the
world she would have avoided ever meeting again had
not fate taken a hand in things.

She slipped into the car and, as he closed the door,
Craig met her gaze. Once again some unseen force
quivered between them, unmistakable and potent.
Masculine magnetism, she rationalised the
unexpected impact; it doesn't mean a thing, not to me.

He put a hand to the ignition and they swung into
the main road where the lights of motor scooters
formed a moving lane of lights in the darkness.

Presently Craig guided the car to a stop amongst the
lorries, cars and motor scooters drawn up haphazardly
near a dimly lighted tavern. He turned to her with his
satirical grin. 'Here we go!'

Together they made their way towards the bar open
to the balmy night. Craig steered her as they threaded
their way amongst the groups gathered around the bar
and the dancing couples. All around them rose a

babel of voices, bursts of laughter, the chink of glasses, and above all the throb of guitars pulsing out into the darkness.

Seated at a table with Craig, Joanne peered through a haze of cigarette smoke, her glance roving over the men and women in the hot crowded room. Her probing glance moved to the noisy groups gathered around the bar where her obvious interest evoked masculine grins, amorous glances and warm invitations to join their group.

'What would you like to drink?' Craig was saying. 'How about the favourite drink of the island, *waiora*? The rule is to ration yourself to two drinks at each tavern,' he told her, 'otherwise you'd never last the distance, not with fifteen nightspots on the island.'

She laughed. 'I'll try a *waiora*. I've got to keep my wits about me tonight, find out all I can.' He had risen to his feet. 'If there's anything to find out!' she mocked in unison with his resonant tones.

As she watched his tall figure moving amongst the crowd around the bar the thought came to her once again. He's easily the most attractive-looking man in the room. Swiftly she thrust the reflection aside. And the most difficult to get on with, she reminded herself.

Her roving glance swept the moving scene around her. Olive-skinned Rarotongans, a smattering of English and European men and women, and from somewhere near at hand she caught an echo of Canadian and American accents. Holiday-makers, no doubt, making a tour of the scattered Pacific islands.

Craig was gone for quite a time, and she caught glimpses of him at the bar apparently in conversation with various men. He's probably enjoying himself immensely, she told herself. Knowing the way he feels about Rick probably he won't even mention his name.

I can't think why I ever believed he would really make enquiries just for me.

When he threaded his way back through the smoke-filled room she leaned towards him eagerly. After all he might have kept his word to her. 'Any luck?'

'Not a thing. Not that I expected to hear anything——'

'Well, I do!' she said with spirit. 'It's worth a try!'

His sceptical glance said it all too plainly.

'I'm not giving up already!' she declared.

Over the rim of his glass his eyes held hers. 'I didn't think you would, knowing you!'

She pushed the damp curls back from her forehead. 'It's awfully hot,' she murmured, 'and so crowded. Is it always like this?'

He grinned. 'This is nothing. Wait a few hours until the place really gets going. Like to call off the missing persons project for tonight? You've had quite a day of it.'

'No! I——' She broke off as a heavily featured young man in jeans and sweatshirt wove an unsteady way in her direction. The next moment she realised that Craig had that hateful glint of amusement in his eyes. He leaned towards her. 'They don't like you to turn the men down for a dance here,' he said softly, 'it's not considered polite on the island.'

She glared at him. 'I know, I know. You told me.'

'Dance?' She looked up into a sweaty, scarlet face and as she moved away with the stranger she threw Craig an angry look over her shoulder. Clearly he was enjoying her discomfiture. He would!

The next moment as she moved to the rhythm of guitars amid the crowd of dancers she told herself that this was what she'd wanted, wasn't it? An opportunity to mix with strangers, especially residents of the island. 'Have you been here long?' She was forced to raise her voice above the rising volume of sound.

Her companion appeared to be concentrating on his footwork. 'Not long enough. Great, isn't it! The firm I work for back in New Zealand sent me over here on business.' He gave a prodigous wink.

As the music crashed to a close she asked the question that meant everything to her. 'You've never been here before?'

'Not me! No such luck! Now that I am, why don't we enjoy it together? If you——'

But Joanne had lost interest in the conversation. She had at that moment caught a glimpse of Craig and his dancing partner. Trust him to pick out the prettiest girl in the room. Blue-eyed and blonde, she was smiling up into his face as though he were someone special. If only the other girl knew!

At that moment a burst of music flooded around her and she became aware of a serious-eyed young man who was hurrying in her direction.

'May I?' She nodded and he swept her into the moving throng. 'What a crush!' Neatly dressed, his brown hair carefully brushed, he appeared to be a young businessman. The sound pulsing around them made conversation difficult but she persevered. Raising her voice above the clamour, she said, 'It's all new to you, this place, is it?'

'Just arrived last night on the plane.' He looked tense and anxious. 'I haven't caught up with things yet.'

'Did you have a good trip?' But she wasn't listening as he endeavoured to explain to her in detail his arrival at the island in the early-morning hours. One phrase of what he was saying caught her attention. 'My first time on the island, or I'd have been prepared for it.'

She realised now that her mission tonight was going to prove more difficult than she had expected. Almost she could admit to herself, never to Craig of course, that maybe it would be advisable for him to get about and meet other men, quiz them about their life-style. After all he was familiar with the island, and what was more important, he was friendly with many of the residents.

As the night wore on and they moved from one crowded tavern to another, her dancing partners continued to vary in age and employment. Young doctors from New Zealand working on a two-year stint at the local hospital, clerical workers sent over to the island by the New Zealand Government, fishermen from local vessels, a member of a film crew making a documentary on dolphins, tourists and promoters of holiday accommodation, travel agents. They all, however, had one characteristic in common. On this island that had become known as the most unspoiled one in the South Pacific, no one she had yet met had any knowledge of a solo yachtsman named Rick or of his craft the *Joanne*.

As the hours wore on it seemed to Joanne that one crowded bar began to look much like another. Now the sounds pulsing out into the night were louder, the cigarette smoke more dense, the talk and laughter shriller. On the open-air dance floors flower-garlanded Rarotongan girls and youths moved with swinging hips and rotating knees to the wild tempo of the native dances. The rhythm was fast and exciting and Joanne's limbs moved automatically to the pulsing drum-beat.

Near morning the crowded scene became blurred to her eyes and she was aware of a dull throbbing at her temples. When Craig made his way through the groups and approached her she didn't enquire whether he had gained any worth-while information about Rick. Somehow there didn't seem much point to the question.

Reluctantly she had to admit to herself that, despite his lack of faith in tonight's search for information regarding Rick, Craig really had made a lot of enquiries on her behalf. It was a task she could not have got through successfully alone, she realised now.

He seemed to tune in on her musing. 'Have you seen enough for tonight?' His keen-eyed glance took in her pale face and shadowed eyes. 'There's one more tavern left to check out, but we'll call it a day if you like. Up to you!'

Swiftly she rallied her sinking spirits. 'No, let's take a look.'

'Right! We're on our way!' He guided her through the throng pressing around them and they moved through the bead curtains and out into the luminous star-strewn night.

The tavern, when they reached it, proved to be the noisiest and most crowded of them all, snatches of song, the throb of guitars and the clink of glasses echoing out into the darkness.

At first Joanne could make out nothing in the dimly lighted, smoke-filled room but a blur of figures thronging a long open bar. As they pushed their way through the crowd at the entrance the heat, moist and oppressive, met them like a blast from an oven. 'I've had enough,' she touched Craig's arm, 'I'll give up for tonight. You go in and I'll wait for you in the car.'

He nodded. 'Good thinking. Won't be long.'

He left her and she gave one last glance towards the crowded bar. At that moment through a haze of cigarette smoke she caught a glimpse of a lanky-looking man with a sandy-coloured beard.

'Rick!' Her glad cry of recognition was lost among the tumult of sound echoing all around. Determinedly she began pushing her way through the throng and at last she reached the tall thin figure. 'Rick?' She tapped him on the shoulder. 'It's me!'

The next moment she found herself looking up into the face of a stranger. He was younger, she realised now, more boyish-looking than Rick.

His expression of astonishment gave way to one of sharp male interest as he stared back at her.

'Sorry,' she muttered, 'I thought you were someone else.'

'I am someone else,' he grinned. 'Wait! Don't go.'

But she pretended not to hear and hurriedly made her way through the crowd to the open doorway and out into the night.

Sick with disappointment, she huddled in Craig's car. It had seemed such a good idea of hers to visit the island taverns in search of information about Rick, but now . . .

Craig remained so long in the tavern that as the time passed hope rose in her once again. At last she caught sight of his tall figure as he strode towards the car and she leaned eagerly from the window. 'You've heard something?' she called to him. 'You've run into someone who knows about Rick?' She began to get out of the car.

'No, no.' He opened the door to the driver's seat and got in beside her.

She sank back dispiritedly then roused herself to say, 'But you picked up something back in the tavern?' she persisted. 'You must have done, you were away for so long.'

He didn't answer for a moment, then he said evenly, 'Nothing really.' There was an odd note in his voice she couldn't interpret.

'You're hiding something from me!' she accused him. 'I can tell by your voice!'

He put a hand to the starter and the motor sprang into life.

'No one in there knew anything definite about your Rick. Does that satisfy you?

She said quickly, 'A rumour, then?'

He shrugged. 'What use are rumours? I got the idea it was information you were after.'

'Yes but . . .' As he turned the car and they headed along the dark road her thoughts were busy. He must have gleaned something about Rick. She threw him a glance and in the dim glow of the dashboard she saw that his face was set and uncompromising. Whatever it was that he had heard in the tavern she knew she wasn't going to hear about it.

'Relax.' He threw her a sideways glance. 'Believe me, if there'd been anything worth reporting I'd pass it on to you.' Something about his closed profile warned her it would be useless to pursue the matter, trivial though it might be.

'You were away an awfully long time in there,' she murmured, 'I thought——'

He tossed her a grin. 'All in the line of duty. I got caught up in a game that was going on.'

'What sort of game?'

'A gambling outfit, actually. Cook Island style with a crab.'

She said incredulously. 'You don't mean a real live crab?'

'Very much alive. He had to be for that sort of game. A lot of guys sit around a table that's marked out in sections. Someone puts a live crab down in the centre and it takes off, scuttles for the edge of the table and wait for it, whoever's lap he lands on pockets the winnings.'

'And you lost?'

'How did you guess?'

She said, very low, 'It seems to be a night for losing, for both of us.'

He made no answer. At least, she told herself, he didn't say, 'I told you so'. No, piped the small devil deep in her mind, but he's thinking it! Everything had turned out just the way he wanted it.

Pull yourself together girl, she scolded herself. It was just an idea to ask around the taverns. Tomorrow Rick might come looking for her. He'd know where to find her because she'd left a message for him at the hotel. Tomorrow.

Stars in the sky were paling against the first flush of dawn when Craig braked the car to a stop outside the unit in the motel. He sat still, one arm thrown carelessly over the back of Joanne's seat, and all at once she was piercingly aware of his nearness. If he tried to kiss her goodnight . . . the thought started a trembling in her.

He didn't. When he spoke his tones were as cool and controlled as ever. 'Look, I've got a heck of a lot of last-minute arrangements to fix up that will take me half the day to sort out. You'll be OK on your own for a while tomorrow?'

'Of course I will!' She forced her voice to an even note, fearful that he might catch the relief in her tone. 'I keep telling you.' No need for him to know how much she preferred him out of the way. There was something about him that did things to her composure, sparked her to a wild anger, affected her in a way she didn't wish to face up to. She said brightly, 'I can have a good look around the kitchen, check up on supplies I'll be needing.

'No rush about that. Do you like swimming?'

Her face brightened and her voice rang with enthusiasm. 'Do I ever!'

'There's just one thing, then. Make certain you wear sandshoes on your feet. A cut out there on the coral can land you with an infection that can put a finish to your holiday.'

'Holiday?' She couldn't resist the gibe.

'Or work, whatever. A word of warning.'

She shifted impatiently in her seat. There seemed to be no end to these lectures of his.

'Don't take off in the lagoon on a board unless there's someone else around. Around this side of the island a wind can spring up from nowhere. You can be swept through the passage in the reef and out to sea, and then believe me you're in big trouble. This high wind can bring treacherous currents that send the sea swooping in and out at dramatic speeds——' He broke off. 'Why are you looking at me like that?'

So those penetrating blue eyes hadn't missed her scornful expression. 'If you must know,' she burst out, 'I happen to be a fairly strong swimmer and I've got certificates to——'

'Nevertheless,' he cut across her triumphant tones, 'out here on the island conditions are a bit different. You'd better believe me.'

'Oh, I do! I do! But you don't believe *me*,' she shot at him accusingly, 'about my swimming ability I mean!'

The careless shrug of his broad shoulders was infuriating. 'I'm warning you, that's all!' He bent on her his cool stare and the thought came unbidden to her mind, how could a man look so devastatingly attractive and yet be so detestable?

'So long as you've got the picture.'

'Oh, I have!' But her eyes sparkled rebelliously. She couldn't wait until morning when he would take himself off from here and she would be alone at the complex. The moment he was out of sight, she promised herself, she would take out one of the glass-bottomed skiffs stacked outside on the sand, prove to him just how mistaken he could be in doubting her ability to handle a light craft with skill, and swim back to shore if need be.

'Do me a favour, will you,' he was saying. 'Do as you're told!

She made a face at him. 'Depends on who tells me!'

'Joanne.' His arm dropped around her shoulders and all at once the atmosphere was tense with emotion. 'Look, there's something——' At the husky softness of his voice, potent as a caress, her heart began to beat wildly and an electric excitement tingled along her nerves.

She was unprepared for the bemusement of his touch and wildly she struggled against the confusion of her senses. Taking evasive action, she said thickly, 'I've got to go,' and fumbled for the door-handle. 'See you tomorrow, then.' She was finding it difficult to say the words that must be said, but somehow she forced them through stiff lips. 'And thanks for trying. Tonight, I mean, about Rick.'

'He was out of the car and standing close to her, too close for her peace of mind. 'My pleasure.'

Once again the traitorous sweetness was taking over her senses. She turned away and with unsteady fingers fitted the key in the lock.

'Night.' He swung around and she was alone, willing herself never again to allow him to affect her in this crazy way. She *must* have imagined the caressing note in his voice!

In the morning when she awoke the sun was beaming through the window on to her face. At that moment the silence was broken by the sound of a car engine starting up and she was just in time to catch a glimpse of a red car sweeping down the driveway.

He'd gone, that maddening employer of hers! Now she could please herself as to what she wished to do. Ridiculous, his warning to her not to go out alone on a boat trip to the reef. An experienced swimmer like herself! She almost laughed aloud at the thought. As if she could be in the slightest danger.

Despite her recent ordeal, the only effect of her frightening experience was a slight feeling of weariness, and that was nothing to worry about. It was the work of only a few minutes to change her cotton nightdress for a faded pink bikini. She made a mug of coffee and as she nibbled a slice of toast her lips tightened mutinously. The needless warning he had handed out to her was quite in character for Craig. Authoritative, interfering, arrogant. But she would prove to him that she was in no way answerable to him.

This was his domain and she might be in his employ, but for heaven's sake, that didn't give him the right to tell her what she could or could not do in her spare time.

Soon she was out in the incredible freshness of the morning, making her way among the bushes starred with tropical blossoms that lined the winding driveway.

A glance down the sloping ground below told her that there were no workmen to be seen there. Maybe they were working on the 'island time' that Craig had told her about. But she didn't want to think of Craig today. Soon she was passing the restaurant with its shuttered windows, then she took a path winding over the sand towards the open-air pavilion with its swimming and diving-gear, towels and snorkels for the use of the guests. From the light craft stacked near by, surfboards, skiffs and kayaks, she chose a skiff with a glass viewing-panel and dragged it over the sand. Ahead of her the sea was a sheet of blue glass shot with myriad flashes of sunlight. How absurd Craig's warning seemed now in this placid scene. Even if there were no one else in sight, what did it matter? She only wanted to guide her skiff out to the coral reef and drift over the water, watching the tropical fish that would be darting out there.

Her bare feet were sinking into the drifts of golden sand as she plodded towards the softly lapping water. As she waded into the sea the crisp touch of the waves was a delight and soon she was guiding her light craft away from the shallows and out towards the broken line of the reef, where breakers were crashing in from the open sea, to splinter in a shower of spray high against the coral.

Out by the reef, she paused. The rippling sea was like watered blue silk and there was no sound but the slight slap-slap of the water against her skiff. The next moment she caught her breath in wonder as she gazed down through the viewing-panel of the skiff at the myriad tiny, vividly hued fish that were darting past in the crystal-clear water. There were butterfly fish, tiny black and white striped creatures and fish in brilliant shades of scarlet, yellow and blue. It was an underwater world of incredible movement, of shoals of tiny jewel-coloured sea-creatures.

For a long while she drifted by the reef, fascinated

by the world of movement and colour below her. Then, without warning, a peal of thunder rolled directly overhead and the sky darkened ominously. Waves splashed over the frail craft and she was carried along by gale-force winds, then the skiff tilted at an angle and she was tossed into the powerful surge of a towering green wall of water. When she could focus her gaze the skiff was already far out of reach.

Half choked with sea-water, she made a frantic effort to swim in the direction of the shore. But another violent gust of wind swept her through the passage in the coral reef and, carried high on the crest of a surging green roller, she was borne into the raging turbulence of the open sea.

Desperately she struggled against the waves, then she realised that she must conserve her strength. It was useless to waste her efforts in a hopeless endeavour to swim back to shore in this sea. Better to keep herself afloat and let herself be carried high on the crests of the rollers and down into the moving green troughs, even though she knew she was being carried ever further from the reef. Wildly she recalled the signal for a person in danger at sea. An upheld hand. But that was back in New Zealand. In these lonely waters there was no one to see or to care.

A shaft of naked fear shot through her. Competent swimmer as she knew herself to be, in this wild ocean where the gale showed no signs of abating she knew she was in a desperate situation.

Close on the thought came another. If she never made it back to the safety of the shore, would *he* care? In that moment of truth it wasn't Rick's half-remembered image that flickered on the screen of her mind but Craig's enigmatic smile and mocking eyes.

Buffeted by the ocean swell, swept further and

further away from shore she lost all count of time.
The world was a surging sea of high waves and deep
waters where nothing else mattered but keeping
herself afloat.

An instinct of self-preservation warned her not to
give way to the insidious drowsiness that was creeping
over her. Think of something else, she told herself, or
someone. Immediately Craig's autocratic tones
returned to mind. She could almost hear his voice. 'I
told you not to go out in the sea alone.' Anger acted on
her failing strength like a shot of adrenalin and a spurt
of energy surged through her chilled body. She would
survive this ordeal, if only to prove to him . . . So help
me God!

'Joanne.' The sound she thought she heard was
borne away on the rushing wind. Now she was
imagining things, wishful thinking born of hope and
desperation.

At that moment she was tossed by a surging
breaker, and, drenched in spray, she could not focus
her gaze for a moment or so. Then another comber
sent her high on the crest and she caught sight of a
man on a surf-ski paddling towards her.

'Hold on! I'm coming!' The masculine tones carried
towards her and now there was no mistaking the call.

'Thank God! Thank God!' A great surge of relief
swept her.

Between deep troughs in the waves she caught
glimpses of the light craft skimming the turbulent
water, then the board was alongside her and Craig's
voice echoed in her ears. 'Come on, grab my hand!
Hold tight!' She grasped his outstretched hand and he
hauled her across the board a moment before a great
wall of water came surging towards them.

'Straddle the board!' For once she didn't mind

obeying his orders. Obediently she stretched in front of him, her hands gripping the sides of the board and her feet clinging to his wet thighs.

Craig sent the narrow craft scything swiftly through the surf and soon they were moving towards the reef passage, slicing through the white spray splintering high around them, to reach calmer water at last as they approached the shore.

Craig guided the board into the shallows then, picking her up in his arms as lightly as if she were a child, he strode up the sandy beach.

Presently he set her down on the pathway. 'Are you OK?' There was an unaccustomed cadence in his low tones.

She managed a wobbly smile. 'I'm fine!' The next moment sea and sky shimmered together and the sunlit scene rocked about her.

When the world around her swam back into focus she had a hazy sensation of being carried in strong masculine arms, pressed so close to Craig's sinewy wet body that she could feel the thick, dark mat of hair on his chest.

A state of dreamy contentment was taking over. It just went to show, she thought hazily, what exhaustion and relief could do to your emotions—cause you to feel this sense of warmth and deep content even although your rescuer happened to be a man you couldn't stand in the ordinary way.

She gave herself up to the pleasure of the moment, dripping sea-water, cold shivers and all! She was almost sorry when he kicked open the door of his unit and with unexpected tenderness laid her gently down on the bed.

'You're cold?'

'A b-bit.' Tremors of chill were running through

her.

'You'd better get out of that wet gear——' He swung around to take a man's robe from a wardrobe. 'Then put this on. Dry off first, though.' He threw her a towel, then another. 'Like me to give you a rub-down?'

'No, no,' she said hastily. With shaking fingers she unclasped the fastening of her bikini top then slipped out of the panties. She towelled herself dry, thankful that he was busy at a cocktail cabinet. Swiftly she pulled on the robe.

'How about your hair?' She looked up to meet his cool-eyed stare. How could she ever have imagined he might have changed in his attitude towards her? Any softening of his feelings towards her was merely temporary, born of the danger from which he had rescued her.

'I can manage.'

Before she could protest further he bent towards her and started rubbing her wet hair with the towel. It was a vigorous action, and yet in some odd way she was enjoying it. There was strength in his well-shaped hands—and something else. An excitement that sent tremors shooting through her. And she knew that this wasn't the effect of chill and exhaustion.

Even more disturbing than his touch on her hair was his closeness. She could feel his breath on her face and her stupid heart was beating fast. His nearness was doing things to her, chasing away the feeling of exhaustion and bringing in its place a wild, sweet happiness.

She struggled to wrench herself back to some sort of sanity. This was Craig, whom she hated more than any other man she had ever met in her life. Remember?

'That's enough!' she said at last. Even to her own ears her voice held a breathless quality. Because of long hours spent in a raging sea? Or could it be the faint tones of a girl who found herself in deeper waters than she could cope with, betrayed by her senses into seductive hidden depths that she knew she must avoid at all costs?

'Down this!' His decisive tones cut across her musing. He was holding towards her a small glass of brandy. 'It will do you good!'

She made a face at him. 'I can't bear the taste.'

'Take it!' His inexorable tone was more in keeping with the man she was familiar with. Anyway, she was too spent to argue with him right now.

The fiery liquid coursing through her veins revived her, and with renewed strength came a realisation of how much she was in his debt.

Dropping down to a chair she played nervously with the cord of the robe. 'It was lucky,' she forced the words through stiff lips, 'that you came along to rescue me. I don't know . . . how to thank you.'

'Forget it. I've been in a surf rescue team for years back home and the old surf-ski I brought with me came in handy.'

'All the same . . .' To break the silence she ran wildly on, 'I suppose you came back here for something you'd forgotten.'

'Not really.' She didn't trust the derisive gleam in his eyes. 'I didn't trust——'

'The weather,' she cut in. 'It blew up out of nowhere, that gale. I just couldn't believe it!'

'Not the weather!'

'What, then?' She raised clear blue eyes to meet his laconic stare.

'You.'

'Me?' Could that surprised squeak be her own voice?

'That's right,' he agreed in his cool, maddening tones. 'I didn't trust the look in your eyes last night.'

'You mean,' she couldn't meet his glance, 'when you were telling me,' she drew a deep breath, '*ordering* me not to go out to the reef unless there was someone else around the place?'

'That's right.'

Striving for control over her runaway emotions, she pushed the cluster of damp curls back from her forehead. 'I wouldn't have thought,' she said very low, 'that you'd have gone away out there beyond the reef—just for me.'

'What are you talking about?' The hard-eyed stare was back in his gaze and she felt sick with humiliation. 'What did it matter who it was? Someone was in a hell of a spot out there and I had to do something about it. Anyone would have done the same. I'll tell you something. You came nearer to drowning today out there in those raging seas than you'll ever know.'

'I do know.' She avoided his gaze. She just knew she would find herself on the answering end of one of his cold, accusing looks. If only the words weren't so hard to say. 'I'm ever so grateful to you for rescuing me, I am really. It's just,' she ran on in a rush of words, 'it bugs me, the way you keep on lecturing me, giving me orders.'

At last she raised her glance to receive the full impact of his angry stare. 'Too bad.' He grinned. 'Now get this straight. I know this island like the back of my hand and you don't! The islands and reefs around these waters are endless and the tides, well, you know what happened out there by the reef today!'

His superior manner, his way of talking down to her as though she were a child, stung her anew. Flooded with hot resentment, she forgot all about being grateful to him.

'So see you don't do it again, Joanne,' she mimicked his stern tones.

'That's right.' His deadpan expression was anything but soothing to her taut nerves. 'Now that we've got that little lot sorted out—hey!' He broke off, his gaze taking in the pallor of her face, her hands wrinkled with immersion in sea-water. Suddenly his tones were tinged with concern. 'You're shaking like a leaf!'

'I'm not!' But her teeth were chattering together. She turned her face aside, muttering half under her breath, 'As if you'd care.'

'I care.' But the cold anger in his eyes looked more as if he longed to shake her, she thought. 'I can't afford to lose you.'

'Me? But I thought you——' A crazy excitement started in her. Then her spirits plunged. 'I nearly forgot. You've just signed up a new chef for your restaurant.'

For a moment something flickered in his eyes, but it was gone almost immediately and she wondered if she had merely imagined his momentary change of expression. He was saying evenly, 'What else?' Suddenly he was glaring down at her, flinging down the covers of the bed. 'Are you going to crawl in there between the sheets and grab some sleep before you catch pneumonia?' He was advancing towards her threateningly. 'Or do I have to make you?' His eyes had darkened and there was no doubt at all but that he meant what he said.

'OK,' she agreed with mock resignation, 'if you say

so—sir!'

He was bending towards her. 'I said—in!'

Hurriedly she dived between the sheets and, pulling the covers up to her chin, she stared up at him, blue eyes wide and wary.

'You can relax.' The sardonic note in his voice chilled her. 'You needn't look at me like that! Half-drowned females don't attract me!' Before she could catch her breath, let alone think up a sufficiently crushing retort, he had jerked down the blind, turned on his heel and closed the door behind him.

She stared after him, breathing fast. Beast! Of all the hateful things to say to her! But it was typical of him really, didn't she know it!

Just as well, another part of her mind reminded her, when his male magnetism—for of course that was all it was—could stir her even against her will. It would be different from now on. She would guard herself against the seductive, exciting spell he seemed to cast on her—if she could. Amazing how chill and exhaustion could put the really important things out of your mind. Even Rick, whom she loved!

CHAPTER SIX

ALMOST at once sleep claimed Joanne, a deep, refreshing oblivion from which she awoke hours later. It took her a few moments to figure out why she came to be lying in bed in an unfamiliar room and wearing a man's white towelling robe. Then realisation came back and she glanced down at her wristwatch, but of course it had been damaged beyond repair and there seemed to be no clock in the unit.

At that moment the peal of the telephone bell shrilled through the room, and sleepily she stretched out her hand towards the bedside telephone.

'Craig here,' came the vibrant masculine tones, 'just checking to find out how you were.'

Still hazy with sleep, she told herself it must surely be the instrument that lent a note of genuine concern to his low tones. Swiftly she pulled her thoughts together. 'I'm feeling fine now, thanks, as good as new!'

'Good enough to come for a run in the car with me?' She must have dreamed up the husky note of concern in his voice for now his tones were as impersonal as ever. 'I'm off to collect a few things in town.'

The nerve of him! He was speaking to her as though there had been no heated words exchanged between them a short time earlier. Half-drowned females had no attraction for him, indeed! The words still rankled. Aloud she said stiffly, 'I really don't think——'

His voice sharpened. 'You're not feeling up to it?'

'It's not that——'

He cut in before she could think up a suitable excuse for avoiding the outing. 'I was counting on you to give me a line on what you'll be needing for the foodstuffs I'm getting in for the restaurant opening.'

He had trapped her neatly, for how could she refuse the invitation when it involved the job he had offered her?

She said stiffly, 'All right, then.'

'OK. I'll call around for you in half an hour.'

Swiftly she returned to her own unit, took a quick shower and found fresh undergarments. Soon she was slipping over her shoulders a sleeveless white cotton top and tying around her slim waist a flaring cotton skirt in muted shades of mauve and pink. She thrust her feet into rubber thongs and ran a comb through the tangle of unruly black curls. Sun-lotion smoothed on her face, a smear of lilac-tinted eyeshadow and a touch of mascara to her lashes completed her toilet.

She had mixed herself a cup of instant coffee and was nibbling a tomato sandwich when she opened the door to Craig.

'You *are* feeling all right?' He eyed her closely but only a slight pallor and the blue shadows around her eyes betrayed her recent ordeal in the turbulent sea. 'Thank heaven for that!' His glance roved around the room. 'Is everything here to your liking? There's nothing else you need? You've only got to tell me——'

She shook her head. 'It's nice.' There was no need to admit that she was enjoying the sense of freedom from anxiety as to being able to stay on the island. Besides, there was something very satisfying in having a place of one's own to live in, even if it was only on a temporary basis. Aloud she murmured, 'There's really everything here that I need.'

'How about rations?' She hadn't realised until this

moment that he had brought a container with him. 'Just to make sure you don't starve while you're waiting for the restaurant opening.'

'I have tea and coffee and fruit drinks,' she protested. 'That will do me.'

'It won't, you know! You'll need a few basics like cheese.' He was stowing away a carton of food in the fridge. 'Yoghurt? What do you fancy? Banana, paw-paw, fruit salad, mango, pineapple? Take your pick. Meal bread, baked right here on the island. Honey? The local bees do a great job with all the flowers around. Breadfruit chips, how's that?'

'It's a feast.' She hesitated a moment. 'Thanks.' She tried to infuse a note of warmth into her voice. 'Care for a coffee?'

'Not just now, thanks. I'll take you up on that another time. Shall we go?'

'Why not?'

As they strolled together out into a blaze of sunshine he said, 'I have to make a stop at the duty-free store.' Carelessly he added, 'There's something I promised myself I'd pick up there for you.'

'For me?' The words came out as an indignant squeak. She tried for dignity. 'I don't want anything.'

'You'll want this. It's something you simply won't be able to do without once we get the show on the road.'

She raised puzzled blue eyes to his face. Could it be he was merely trying to rile her, as was his usual custom? Yet he seemed sincere enough.

But of course. The thoughts raced through her mind. Her wristwatch that had been ruined for ever in the collision between the bike and his car. But a gold watch, even when purchased at a duty-free store, was an expensive item, and she couldn't, she wouldn't accept such a gift from him.

As she seated herself in the car she threw him a suspicious glance. 'Nothing personal, then. I don't want anything personal from you.'

He bent on her his cool maddening stare. 'Why would I do that?

She felt a hot tide of embarrassment sweep over her. Damn him, he had a knack of putting her in the wrong every time. But he wouldn't get away with this. She would refuse to accept his gift whatever it might be. She would hand it right back to him, wipe the self-satisfied expression from his face.

'I won't take it,' she persisted stubbornly. The glint of amusement in his eyes sparked her to say hotly, 'You'll be wasting your money if you buy anything for me!'

'Not this time!' His heart-stopping grin took her by surprise and her stupid heart missed a beat. 'All part of the deal!'

They were taking the winding driveway leading down to the road and Craig's gaze was fixed on the highway ahead. 'Changed your mind about your boyfriend yet?'

Joanne's soft lips firmed. 'I don't know what you mean,' she said tightly.

'Oh, yes, you do.' He tossed her a swift sideways glance. 'The missing persons project?'

She fought the anger that was rising in her like a dark cloud. It helped, she found, if she gritted her teeth and lifted her small square chin. 'Of course I haven't changed my mind about Rick. I keep telling you. I'll find him or he'll find me.' To her chagrin there was a betraying wobble in her voice. 'One of these days.'

'And if he's changed his mind about you?'

'Why do you keep saying that?' she flung at him.

'You don't give him a chance,' she accused him scornfully, 'you've got no faith in anyone!'

'And you've got too much for your own good!'

'So *you* say!' Her eyes were shooting sparks. 'Rick would never let me down.' She added with confidence, 'I just know.'

'Good for you!' A sardonic smile twisted his lips.

The angry silence lasted all the way to the main road. As she stared wrathfully out of the window Joanne told herself that it could last for ever so far as she was concerned.

The next moment they swept around a bend and, forgetting all abut her aggravating companion, she cried out in delight, 'Look! A wedding couple! They're just coming out of the church!'

'Of course,' came the infuriating masculine tones, 'you're interested in weddings just now, aren't you?'

But she refused to allow him to draw her into a futile discussion on the chances of her and Rick being married to each other here on the island. 'I'm interested in this one,' she snapped. 'I've never seen an island wedding.'

'Now's your chance.' He was braking to a stop at the side of the road. Joanne watched, fascinated, as the young Rarotonga couple, smiling and laughing and surrounded by friends and relatives, made their way along the path cutting between the spreading green lawns of the church grounds.

All at once the crowd parted and Joanne leaned forward in her seat. 'There's a strip of material laid all the way to the church gates and the wedding couple are walking on it!'

'That's right.' His cool tones broke across her excited accents. 'The idea is that the couple's feet don't touch the ground until a long time later.'

'It's all so beautiful,' she murmured. Something about

the remoteness of the island, the unfamiliar lifestyle, touched her. 'They look so much in love, those two.'

He was gazing ahead. 'If you want to see a romantic honeymoon vehicle, take a look at the car that's pulling in by the gates. Now you can get a better view.'

He was leaning over her, so close she could feel his breath on her cheek and catch the clean fresh tang of lime aftershave.

'Joanne.' His body, warm through the thin cotton of his shirt, was close, suffocatingly close. Her thoughts were in a turmoil and a warm sweet tide of feeling was rushing through her body, something over which she had no control. The powerful masculine attraction she had sensed before had taken over and she was enjoying the experience. If she had any will-power at all she would draw away from him instead of just . . . just . . . Her limbs seemed to have turned to jelly and her traitorous senses wanted to stay close to him for ever.

'Now you can see something!' He straightened and Joanne dazedly tried to drag her rioting senses back to sanity. She must have imagined that for a crazy moment he shared her wild excitement. But she was good at imagining things where he was concerned, she told herself, for now his tones were his usual calm accents. Now she knew she had only imagined the soft note in his voice, almost like a caress, when he had murmured her name. She must be out of her mind to dream up such fancies.

For a moment she gazed towards the wedding party without taking in the colourful scene. Then realisation came back with a rush. 'All those flowers,' she said, 'there isn't a spot of the wedding car that isn't covered with them.' She watched as the smiling bridal couple got into the vehicle. It took quite a time but at last the car pulled away, friendly calls and laughter and good wishes echoing after the blossom-covered vehicle.

'I wonder where they will go now.' She spoke her thoughts aloud.

'Around the island and back,' came his cool rejoinder. 'There's nowhere else to go!'

'Oh! It seems a bit of a let-down, just around the island.'

'Not to the happy couple it isn't! Quite the opposite. There'll be lots of stops on the round trip.'

'To see friends, you mean?'

'That's right. At every stop they'll be given wedding gifts, all manner of things. A complete outfit of clothing at every call, but otherwise it's all pretty functional stuff usually, brooms, kitchen utensils, cups. And the older women are dab hands at making embroidered quilts. Some of them are quite remarkable, heirloom-type of things that are handed down in the family. You know?'

'Don't the young women make them?'

'Not now. They've lost the knack or the inclination.'

'I don't blame them,' Joanne said with spirit. 'The young women nowadays will have heaps more fun things to do than staying at home with their families, sewing quilts. So even way out here, women are changing their ideas. And a good thing too,' she ran on. 'I bet that no island girl of today would sit at home meekly doing what her husband told her to do.'

He gave a guffaw of laughter. 'You're probably right at that!'

His tone was deceptively bland, much too agreeing, and she threw him a suspicious enquiring glance. The lurking triumphant light in his eyes was infuriating. 'In Rarotonga the women have always been people in their own right, strong and outspoken. Wives are partners, not downtrodden females.'

Something in his tone told her it was the truth, and

despite her distrust of him and the fact that he would say anything to annoy her, she believed him.

Presently they were back in the car, taking the highway edging the sea, and passing small sheltered bays where golden sands glittered in the sunshine and waves caressed the reef.

The sleepy town of Avarua dozed in the afternoon sunshine, the road shaded by tropical red-leaved trees and waving coconut palms. In the shade of flame trees a group of islanders and tourists chatted together as they awaited the arrival of the local bus.

Craig braked to a stop at an open market where Rarotongan women were seated on coconut mats beside woven baskets overflowing with tropical fruits and freshly-gathered vegetables. Soon Joanne and Craig were getting back into the car, their arms laden with golden paw-paw, bananas and fresh pineapples.

As he put a hand to the starter she wrinkled her nose at him. 'No avocados?'

He grinned. 'No appreciation of them here. They grow wild all over the place, but the islanders feed them to the pigs, would you believe?'

'Really?' She eyed him incredulously.

'But if you're tempted,' he grinned down at her, 'you can always help yourself to fruit growing along the roadside or in anyone's garden for that matter. It's the custom on the island.'

She laughed. 'I'll keep it in mind.'

The next moment she reminded herself that she loathed the man. Why must she keep forgetting? Blame the champagne day. All this warmth and colour and pervading air of relaxation must be going to her head.

Soon they were driving past small timber stores of another age where vividly coloured frocks, *pareus* and shirts swung in the breeze on open verandas. Beyond the entrances Joanne caught glimpses of woven baskets and wood carvings, shell ornaments and woven fans.

'Here we go!' Craig had come to a stop outside a sprawling building with a long open porch. 'You can give me a hand with the foodstuffs. It shouldn't be difficult for you, there won't be too much choice!'

As they made their way between the wide aisles Joanne selected her basic requirements for the restaurant work and before long Craig was piling stacks of grocery items into cardboard cartons and placing them in the boot of the car.

They moved on and further down the street he braked the vehicle to a stop among a scattering of motor scooters and trucks drawn up haphazardly outside a large modern store. Wide display windows featured women's fashion frocks, recent model swimsuits and bikinis, men's wear printed in tropical designs of fish and seashells. There were stacks of sunhats and beach umbrellas, toiletries and fishing-gear and all the holiday articles popular with tourists who were escaping the mild New Zealand winter to bask in the balmy sunshine of an unspoilt South Pacific island.

'Come on inside.' Craig was opening the passenger door for Joanne. 'You might like to get some duty-free perfume or a camera.'

'Not me.' No need to explain that she had no spare cash to spend on such luxury items.

'Take a look inside anyway!' Together they strolled into the attractively decorated interior where the olive-skinned saleswomen looked relaxed and welcoming and the accents of Canadian, American and English tourists echoed in the spacious room.

Joanne went with Craig to the duty-free department of the store, and while he made his purchases her idle

gaze roved over the glass display cases with their
scintillating array of jewellery, ropes of pearls, gold and
silver bracelets and brooches set with jade and the rose-
pink coral of the island.

All at once her gaze was drawn to a gold ring set with
a single pearl. The apricot-golden lustre of the gem
fascinated her. Somewhere at some time she had heard
about pink pearls. The thought niggled in her mind but
memory eluded her.

'You won't see many of those pearls around.' Craig
had come to join her. Tall, quietly spoken, just a man.
So why did the ordinary-type store seem suddenly to
have taken on a sort of magic, everything all at once
exciting, *wonderful*! And for no reason at all.

She turned a sparkling face towards him but his eyes
were cool and remote, scarcely interested. Someone
familiar with the island discussing a display of jewellery
with a girl who was just a tourist—or near enough.

'I'd love to own that ring,' she breathed. 'If only——'
The words died away on a sigh. In the present state of
her finances . . .

'Don't kid yourself!' His curt tones cut across her
wistful accents. 'If you're counting on your Rick
handing you one as an engagement ring you haven't a
hope in hell!'

She flung him a resentful glance. 'I didn't say——'

'No, but you were hoping——'

'What if I were? What's wrong with that?'

'Everything so far as you're concerned!'

'I know! I know!' Her blue eyes blazed. 'I just don't
believe what you say, that's all!'

She drew a deep breath, furious with herself for being
drawn into a verbal encounter with him once again
regarding Rick, annoyed with Craig because of his
defeatist attitude towards the man she loved.

'And if you're thinking of buying anything here for me,' she eyed him angrily, 'please don't bother.' The thought of being forced into a position of having to accept an expensive gift from him was unendurable. Far wiser for her to stop him right now from purchasing a gold watch for her. 'So if you've got any ideas in that direction——' Her voice trailed into silence, for something about his cool stare was throwing her into a state of confusion. 'As I told you, I don't want anything from you, especially anything expensive.'

'Who said anything about it being expensive?' His pale eyes held the mocking glint she knew only too well.

'I——' She broke off, aware that the girl behind the counter was eyeing them with interest.

'Would you like me to show you the pearl ring?' she asked Craig. Her gaze moved to Joanne's face. 'I know *you* are interested!' Her smile was meaningful.

'Please,' said Craig. The assistant handed it to him and he gave the ring in its velvet-lined box a cursory glance. 'OK, I'll take it.' He put a hand to his pocket and drew out his cheque book.

Joanne watched in horrified silence as he wrote out the cheque. The tell-tale colour flooded her cheeks. If he dared to try to hand her the expensive ring. Surely he couldn't, he wouldn't—and yet——

He was stowing away the tiny jewel-case in the pocket of his denim jeans. 'Robyn will be over the moon when I give her this.'

'Robyn?' she said stupidly. A chill was creeping through her body.

He nodded. 'My right-hand man, or woman rather! I'll tell you something, it means a lot to me having her with me to give me a hand with the motel venture. There's just no one like her.'

Joanne tried to focus her attention on his words,

but a desolate feeling of loss and emptiness blotted out everything else. She had a queer feeling of having glimpsed something rare and precious that was now beyond her grasp for ever.

His glowing words seemed to come from a distance. 'She's crazy about the pink pearls over here. I've been waiting a long time hoping to pick one up at the store here. The timing's just right too, she won't have to wait long for it, only a week or so.' For a man who had purchased a special ring for his girl he seemed to be very matter of fact. But then, she reminded herself, he would never show any emotion. She doubted if he had the capacity to feel deeply, except when it came to dislike, and that he kept for her.

She wrenched her mind back to his jubilant tones. 'Robyn told me that if ever I was lucky enough to come across a ring set with one of these pearls, to grab it before anyone else did and to hell with the cost! Just wait until I show her this.'

The strange, odd feeling was fading. It couldn't have had any connection with her stupid assumption that the ring Craig had just purchased was to be given in love to the woman in hs life. That was plainly ridiculous. No, the moment of weakness would be merely the after-effects of her misadventure in the sea earlier in the day. What else? What's the matter with you? she chided herself. He means nothing to you or you to him. For clearly he has his own love life all sorted out.

'They come from one tiny island further north and even there they're hard to find. The women on the island dive deep to get the shells and sometimes they're lucky enough to find a pearl.'

Suddenly Joanne was light-hearted with a strange sense of relief. 'The women!' Her laughter rang out.

'Tell me, why is it always the women on these islands who do everything worth while?'

He grinned. 'It's part of the culture here. The women have all the say. They're in control of the island and have been for centuries. Married men do as their wives tell them, and believe me they do tell them, in no uncertain terms!'

'Good for the women!' She eyed him challengingly.

'You should get along fine in Rarotonga,' she suspected his quirky smile, 'a girl like you!'

She didn't trust his deceptively soft accents. For if there was one thing she had learned about the boss it was that he didn't toss compliments about lightly, especially where she was concerned. 'What's that supposed to mean?'

His eyes were brilliant with a look she couldn't fathom. 'Can't you guess?'

All at once enlightenment dawned on her. 'Oh, I get it!' A fugitive smile lighted her face and dimples flickered around her lips. 'Well,' she said wryly, 'I do *try*. But I don't seem to get very far, not with you.'

'All for your own good,' he observed in his maddening, peremptory way.

'You mean,' she demanded, 'like my going out beyond the reef?'

His eyes darkened. 'You should have listened to me!'

To change the subject she said quickly, 'You don't listen to me about that gift you've been insisting on giving me.'

'Not to worry.' She caught the glint of amusement in his eyes. 'It's something you can make good use of.'

Her eyes glittered with anger. 'All the same——'

'Don't argue, Joanne.'

'I can't let you,' she glared at him, 'I simply refuse.'

'Too late, I've already done the deed. It's right here in

my pocket. Now don't get impatient. You'll get it, all in good time.'

'*Impatient!*' She drew a deep breath. 'That's the last thing I'd be. And you know it. I'll give it right back to you.'

'You haven't got it yet.'

'You're being ridiculous,' she hissed, 'and those two sales girls standing behind you are listening to every word we say.'

He swung around and the girl assistants hurriedly moved away.

'What of it?' he enquired calmly. 'They'll put it down to a lovers' quarrel. Quite interesting for them. It'll make their day.' He raised his voice. 'Come along, my love, let's go home.' He sent her a wide grin then threw an arm purposefully around her waist and guided her among the stalls and out to the wide-open doors.

Out in the street at last she flung herself free of his encircling arm and marched angrily towards the car. He didn't seem to notice her silence as he fitted the key into the ignition and drove off, weaving a course between the island girls and youths on their motor scooters.

They were skirting the sands of a sheltered bay when he tossed a package into her lap. 'For you.'

She hesitated. What could she do? Short of forcing it back on him, which seemed somehow childish. And anyway she did owe him quite a lot. Her life? The thought made her reconsider her decision and grudgingly she picked up the small flat parcel from her lap. She said coldly, 'If you insist.'

He pulled up the car on the shoreline where waves were creaming in on golden sands. A flat jeweller's box? The thoughts were flying through her mind. If he had dared to buy her a gold watch, after all she had said to him on the subject . . .

She realised he was eyeing her closely. 'Aren't you going to open it?'

'Now?' She played for time.

'Why not?' She didn't trust the dancing devil in his eyes one little bit. No doubt it signified he was planning a victory over her.

Resentment gave way to curiosity. 'All right, then.' She slit open the wrapping to reveal a soft-covered booklet decorated in simple flower motifs and entitled *Recipes of the Cook Islands*.

The words she had planned to say died on her lips. To think she had half expected him to hand her a gold watch, and he presented her with a cookbook. She was sick with humiliation.

'Thanks very much,' she said huffily.

'Aren't you going to read it?' Damn him, he knew all too well she hadn't expected a gift of this sort. For sure he'd have that triumphant glint in his eyes again. He had.

She flicked open a page. 'Anyway,' she said, 'it's no use to me. All the recipes are in the Rarotongan language.'

'And in English! Take a look on the opposite page!' He was grinning, positively enjoying her discomfiture. The neatly wrapped package was a subtle reminder of his lack of faith in her ability to cope with the specialised requirements of her restaurant job. She could have wrung his neck!

She lifted her chin defiantly. 'But I don't need it. I think I can handle the menus at your motel without the help of the local ladies. They might come in handy, the recipes, in an emergency maybe.'

Immediately the words had left her lips she would have given anything to have called them back. For he was looking more smug and triumphant than ever. Swiftly she qualified the statement. 'That is,' she murmured carelessly, 'if I ever get around to studying them.'

'No harm in boning up on the traditional Umuki food, meals cooked island-style in earth ovens.'

'For heaven's sake!' Impatiently she brushed the suggestion aside. 'I know all about how the Maori folk back home cook their pork and *kumeras* in earth ovens for a *hangi*. That should be near enough.'

All at once his eyes were cold steel. 'Near enough isn't good enough for the Kia Orana.'

The censorious tone of his voice was more than she could stand. 'All right, *all right!*' She flung the book down and glared balefully out of the window. She hated him all over again. Never mind if he had saved her life and offered her a job, he was still cold and hateful and autocratic.

Without another word he started the car and they sped alongside the shimmering blue sheet of the sea. Joanne, still seething with anger, was scarcely aware of her surroundings. She pitied that unfortunate girl-friend of his, she really did.

He seemed to tune in with her thoughts. 'I'm lucky having Rob to help with things at the motel.' All at once his vibrant tones rang with enthusiasm. 'I can rely on her to take care of just about everything in the place, if need be. We worked together at a motel I was managing in the Bay of Islands back in New Zealand, and I couldn't fault her. She'll help me with the books, arrange transport, and she'll be indispensable when it comes to keeping the guests happy. With her on the job I can relax about all sorts of details that would be a headache otherwise.'

'She'll be entertainments manager?' Joanne asked for something to say.

'And the rest!' She had never heard him sound so

animated. 'She's a first-class person to have around
the place. Takes care of all bookings, knows just how
to make guests feel welcome and wanted and
entertained. If there are any complaints, Rob will sort
them out, no problem. She manages to keep on good
terms with the staff too, keeps an eye on the dining-
table——'

Joanne's lips tightened. 'Does she indeed?'

His mind, however, was still on the other girl. 'Not
that you'd notice her but she's just around, watching
in case any of the folk under her care need extra
attention, special foods, a diet. I tell you, when it
comes to this sort of job, she's a natural.' He sounded
so enthusiastic that Joanne found herself taking an
irrational dislike to this paragon. His glowing tributes
to Robyn made her uneasily aware of how little she
knew about so many things here, like pushbikes and
island lagoons and even her restaurant job. If only she
had some actual work experience.

Aloud she said, 'Does she know the island?'

It was no use. She might have known the answer to
the question, for Craig sounded more than ever
excited about his entertainments manager. 'She was
brought up here, just as I was, and came back for
holidays later. We've known each other for ever.' His
eyes were thoughtful. 'It'll be great having her here
with me at the Kia Orana.'

A devil of perverseness made her say, 'And does she
always do as you tell her?'

He chuckled, an attractive sound deep in his throat.
'I don't need to tell her. She's so efficient you
wouldn't believe.'

No, I wouldn't. Joanne said the words to herself.
Aloud she said, 'Have you told her—about me? You
know, the cooking job?'

His tone was enigmatic. 'Sure, she knows.'

Trust her not to leave well alone, but she seemed unable to stop herself. 'And what,' she enquired lightly, 'did she think about that?'

'Actually——'

'I know,' she cut in, 'she thought you were taking a risk. Don't tell me. As a businesswoman she'd remind you that the venture depends a whole lot on the reputation of the restaurant. If guests don't care much for the menus, they don't come back again for their holidays. I suppose,' she flung at him bitterly, 'you told her that I wasn't experienced in the job, not really.'

His voice hardened. 'I told her you were on trial for three months.'

Joanne was trying to get the better of her temper and once again she wasn't making much headway. 'I don't know,' she said in a low voice that vibrated with anger, 'why you take so much notice of this—this Robyn.' She flashed him a challenging glance. 'I thought that you were the boss of the outfit.'

His voice was ice-cold, 'You've noticed? You'll understand what I'm getting at when you get to know her.'

Will I? Joanne very much doubted it. One autocratic boss would be quite sufficient for her here without another perfectionist, she thought crossly.

'She has a knack of keeping everything running along smoothly,' Craig was saying. It seemed to Joanne he couldn't stop himself singing the other girl's praises. The way he was enthusing about Robyn one would think he was in love with her. Maybe he was. Joanne couldn't understand why the thought should be so . . . disturbing.

One thing, her thoughts ran on, Craig and Robyn understood one another and were close friends.

Friends, or long-time lovers? She pushed the thought aside. What did it matter to her anyway?

Wrenching her mind back to his attractive tones, she thought how different he looked when, carried away by enthusiasm, he forgot who he was talking to. So different that she could almost imagine that a girl who didn't know his real nature night find herself falling in love with him. Not her, of course, she hurriedly qualified the crazy thought. Not this girl!

CHAPTER SEVEN

LYING in bed that night, Joanne was drifting on the edge of consciousness when a stab of realisation brought her to full awareness. Now she knew, well, she had a fair idea, where Rick was to be found. All she need do was to go and see him. Close on the thought came another: and refuse to allow herself to be influenced by that interfering Craig. This time she would go her own way regardless of his annoying interest in her affairs.

She couldn't sleep for excitement and, soon after dawn had flushed the eastern sky, she slipped into her bikini, grabbed a towel and made her way down the path winding between coconut palms to the sand, cool to the touch of her bare feet.

Except for a windsurfer rounding a point of a bay, the place seemed deserted. Just the way she liked it, she mused happily, which meant of course that the boss wasn't out taking an early-morning swim.

Soon she was running into the water, a-dazzle with myriad flashes of sunlight, then she was striking out with clean, sure strokes for the crystal-clear depths ahead. For a long time she enjoyed the caressing touch of the waves, then at last she waded out through the shallows, drops of sea-water showering up around her.

'Joanne!' She knew the voice only too well and spun around as a windsurfer with a scarlet sail came skimming over the water towards her.

She pushed the sea-drenched hair away from her

eyes and stood watching as the craft came nearer. She couldn't take her eyes from Craig. The sun burnished his lean-muscled frame, accentuating his splendid physique as he stood braced against the blue sky guiding his frail craft inshore. Wearing swimming trunks the exact shade of his sun-bronzed skin, he seemed to her at that moment like a young Greek god cast in bronze. Conflicting emotions tore at her: admiration, resentment and a reluctant pull of the heart. If only he weren't so devastatingly attractive.

The next moment he had leaped down into the shallows beside her, then began pulling the wind-surfer over the wet sand. She splashed along beside him. For something to say, she remarked, 'And I thought I was the first one down on the beach today.'

He grinned and she caught a flash of strong, white teeth in a sun-darkened face. 'Surprise! Surprise!'

So he had decided to ignore their stormy argument of yesterday. Well, it was a game at which two could play.

As he hauled his craft up on the shore, she dropped down on the beach, watching him. What was the matter with her? she chided herself. Just because he had looked to her like a young Greek god as he guided his craft over the waves . . . She hated him, remember?

The next moment he had come to join her, shaking sea-water from his hair. He turned towards her, eyeing her with his disturbing look, and suddenly once again she was piercingly aware of his nearness. To break the spell, she said the first words that came to mind. 'I didn't know—that you had a windsurfer here.'

'I'm getting in a good supply for the holiday season.' All at once his eyes held their dancing glint. 'I'll have to take a risk on the know-alls among the guests who won't heed a warning when it's handed to them.'

Instantly she was on the defensive. She eyed him challengingly. 'Like me, you mean?'

'I didn't say that.'

'You didn't need to! Anyway,' she ran on before he could lecture her once again in the matter of water-safety, 'I've got something to tell you.' All at once excitement took over and she ran on breathlessly, 'You wouldn't believe——'

'Try me.' His cool accents cut across her excited tones. 'You've got news of your Rick, right?'

She nodded. 'And it's all because of the pearl rings we saw in Avarua yesterday.'

'I told you you'd have to produce your fiancé first.' His voice had the mocking, disbelieving inflection he seemed to keep especially for any mention of Rick. It was almost as if he were jealous of the other man. She brushed the absurd thought aside.

'Oh, you never understand about Rick!' she burst out. She glared down at his imperturbable face. 'You just don't care about him, do you!'

'Not particularly.' He was lying on his back, hands crossed behind his head, squinting against the sun-glare. 'Are you telling me you've discovered his whereabouts?'

'Not exactly.' Meeting the mocking gleam in his eyes she looked away. 'But I will,' she assured him, 'now that I know where he is.'

'You actually know?' He sounded incredulous.

'Well, near enough. You see,' she rushed on, 'I thought of something last night, something that Rick told me once. He said that if ever he got into financial difficulties during his island-hopping trip, if he needed urgent repairs done to his yacht, he'd head for an island in the Cook Group where divers can find pearls. He's an experienced deep-sea diver, and don't you see,' her voice rang with excitement; 'it all ties in? He was here recently, then left again, but he'll be coming back.'

'Oh, yes,' he seemed scarcely interested, 'according to the information you got from the sailor friend you met up with in the café?'

'That's right,' she said airily. 'The one you didn't believe was telling me the truth. But *I* believe him!'

'Good for you.' Her lips tightened. Sarcastic brute.

'So I take it,' he said, 'that you're planning on taking a trip to this special island where the pearls are to look him up?'

'You bet your life I am!' The sudden switch from hopelessness to almost certain success in her search for Rick was making her voice ring with happiness.

He raised himself on an elbow, his lazy glance all at once deep and compelling. 'Tell me, just how do you propose to do that?'

She was ready for that one. 'No problem. I'm going down to the wharves this morning. You know the fishing-boats that are moored there? Well, I've got enough funds left to charter a boat to the island. The fishermen will be sure to know where it is. It can't take all that long to sail there and back.'

'Two hours in a motor boat.'

'Oh, is that all?' She was elated. 'It can't take all that much time, then, to make the trip in a fishing boat.'

'With you, it could take for ever.'

'*What?*'

'Look,' his intent gaze held her against her will, 'you'll be taking one hell of a risk haring off on that trip in a fishing-boat. Around these islands a storm can blow up out of nowhere. You know what happened the other day when you were out in the lagoon.'

She raised her eyes heavenwards. Wait for it! Another lecture. 'I wish now,' she muttered half under her breath, 'that I hadn't told you about Rick.'

He ignored that and went on as though she hadn't spoken.

'Believe me, if the boat cracks up or the weather blows up rough from the east you'll be in big trouble. It would be a matter of swimming to safety. That's fine for the locals, they're used to long swims, but you're not.'

The discomfiting thought struck her that she had been near exhaustion when he had rescued her from the turbulent waters of the open sea. She brought her mind back to his even tones.

'Do you really reckon it's worth it, this trip you're so excited about? If you do find Rick, how do you know——'

Her eyes were shooting sparks. 'I know what you're thinking!' she flung at him. 'But you're way off beam! Rick wouldn't be interested in any other woman but me, not seriously. Not ever,' she amended firmly as she caught the sardonic lift of his brows. 'As I told you, neither of us has bothered about anyone else ever since we met at high school.' She was running on wildly, her voice a little out of control, something to do with the mocking look in his eyes. 'And if that doesn't mean something——' She broke off, cheeks flushed and eyes blazing defiantly.

'Oh, sure, it means a lot!' She didn't trust the ironical lift of his well shaped lips.

'When you meet Rick you'll see how right I am! And you will meet him pretty soon,' she added confidently, 'maybe tonight.'

'Maybe.'

It was his tone of voice that made her furious with him. 'You won't put me off the idea of the trip, whatever you say,' she muttered stubbornly.

'I've got a better idea. My own boat's having an engine check-up she'll be OK and rarin' to go by tomorrow. So why don't I take——'

For a moment she hesitated, then she shook her head. 'I don't think——'

'Why not?' He shot the words at her. 'What difference can one day make? Time doesn't matter all that much out here in the Cooks.'

'It does to me!' She eyed him defiantly. 'It matters a lot!'

'All the same,' his tone hardened, 'you'd better let me take you.'

'Thanks, but I . . .' Her words died away. She was acutely aware of the disturbing glance that rested on her lips then moved to the vivid blueness of her eyes. Her senses were in wild confusion and there was a breathless quality in her voice. 'I would rather . . .'

He moved closer and she was motionless, something stirring deep within her. He said huskily, 'Shall I make up your mind for you?' Then he was bending over her, his hands caressing her face, his mouth seeking hers. Powerless against the disturbing caress of his touch, she could feel the warmth of his sinewy chest pressed against her body. At last, dazed and trembling, she drew herself free.

I'm crazy, she scolded herself, to feel this way about him. What was a kiss? A nothing thing to him. It meant nothing to her either, and yet . . . In an effort to wrench herself back to sanity she got to her feet, fighting her way through the seductive mists of dangerous awareness.

Avoiding his gaze she dusted the sand from her

knees then stooped to pick up her towel. With an
effort she made her voice light and carefree. 'I'm off.'
Abruptly she turned away and began to plod over the
thick drifts of golden sand. 'To the wharves,' she
threw back over her shoulder, and waited for his
protesting tones. But he simply ignored her call. He
was lying back on the sand, eyes closed against the
sun-glare. So much for a kiss!

Why was she trembling? she asked herself as she
reached the unit. If this was the way his idle caress
affected her she had best avoid the dangerous
charisma she sensed in him. Anyway, she reminded
herself as she showered and towel-dried her hair, she
would soon be reunited with Rick, and that was all
that really mattered. Wasn't it?

Soon she was pulling on bra and panties and white
pedal-pushers. She buttoned the loose shirt of
turquoise-coloured cotton, open at the throat. Rick
had always liked her to wear that shirt. Then she
thrust her feet into pale blue sneakers.

As she mixed a mug of instant coffee and toasted a
slice of bread the disturbing thought crossed her mind
that she could find herself in an awkward position
should she not have sufficient money to pay for the
boat trip to the island. She just couldn't ask Craig for
a loan. It was a habit she seemed to have fallen into
since coming to the island, she thought worriedly,
casting herself on his reluctant mercy. But not this
time! Nor would she swallow her pride and allow him
to take her to the pearl island tomorrow.

Suppose he should offer to take her to the wharves!
The daunting thought made her hurriedly throw into
her shoulder-bag sunscreen lotion, a comb, a small
mirror. Today of all days she must look her best.

Presently she was hurrying down the dusty driveway, a woven straw sunhat swinging from her hands and dark curls tumbling around her shoulders. Somehow it felt all wrong, hurrying in the heat of the island with its relaxed life-style, but then, she mused grimly, the locals didn't have to contend with Craig and his overbearing ways.

She was in luck, for as she reached the main road on the island the bus came into sight and with relief she waited at the stop, then climbed up the step and squeezed herself into a seat.

The vehicle was crowded with Rarotongan women, with blossoms tucked in thier dark tresses and holding woven baskets on their knees. Evidently they were bound for the market. Friendly greetings were beamed towards her from smiling faces and soft voices and laughter echoed around her as the women chatted happily together.

Impatient now to reach her destination, Joanne found herself chafing at the seemingly endless stops along the way where a smiling, unhurried island woman or a group of friends boarded the vehicle. It seemed to her an age before at last the road curved to come in sight of the harbour. Eagerly she craned her neck, letting the wind from the open window have its way with her streaming hair.

Her anxious gaze scanned the wharves where a trading-schooner had berthed during the night. And glory be, she breathed a sigh of relief, there at the farthest wharf was moored a local fishing-boat, old and weathered but no doubt seaworthy even in rough seas, despite Craig's gloomy predictions.

But she wouldn't think of him today, she had other more important matters on her mind. The most important thing in her life actually. Her spirits rose anew at the thought of Rick. They'd have so much to catch up on. What a lot they would have to talk about, she and Rick, so many experiences to relate since they had parted. *So much explaining to do.* Now where could that thought have come from? Craig probably. It was the kind of off-putting thing he would say. Anything to dissuade her from searching for Rick.

When they reached the quiet little town of Avarua the rest of the passengers, encumbered with baskets and accompanied by small children, took a long time to dismount and to Joanne it seemed an age until at last she dropped down to the grassy area of the bus stop.

A fresh breeze ruffled the waves sending water dashing against the wharves as Joanne hurriedly made her way towards the fishing-boat. When she reached the vessel there didn't appear to be much activity on the weathered craft, but the next moment a Rarotongan man of middle age appeared on the deck.

'Oh, please,' she called down to him from the timbers of the wharf above.

He glanced up at the small dark-haired girl, her face alive with excitement, gazing down at him.

'Could you take me for a day trip?'

Smilingly he nodded. He seemed to Joanne to be a typical islander, relaxed, pleasant, quietly spoken. 'Where would you like to go, miss?'

She hesitated. 'I don't know the name. It's a small island further north where the pink pearls are found. Do you know the one I mean?'

His smile broadened. 'I can take you there.'

'That would be wonderful! How much would it cost?'

He named a sum so modest that she breathed a sigh of relief. 'That's all right then.' She could scarcely contain her elation.

Soon she had crossed the gangway and was looking

up at him. 'How soon can we leave?' she enquired eagerly. 'Right away?'

'When my friend comes.'

'Oh!' Her eyes clouded with disappointment.

'He will come.' It was the only satisfaction she could glean from the seaman, who continued to lean on the rail gazing out to the harbour. He looked entirely unperturbed, she thought impatiently, as if an hour or so one way or the other didn't matter one little bit. Maybe it didn't to him!

An hour and a half later, however, the boat was still moored at the wharf. 'Couldn't you go and find your friend?' she asked the seaman in desperation.

He shook his head. 'He could be away working on his land.'

Joanne bit her thumbnail. 'Couldn't you take the boat out yourself?'

Once again he shook his head. 'He'll come,' he said placidly and resumed his gazing out to sea.

But would he? she wondered uneasily. Obviously the men were partners and a special charter trip would be one they hadn't allowed for today.

Nevertheless . . . An interminable hour dragged by. Would she ever accustom herself to island ways, train herself to become a part of the leisurely way of life instead of allowing herself to get into a tizz about a delay such as this? If only the trip weren't so important to her.

Lost in her thoughts, she was scarcely aware of the craft that came hurtling across the water towards her until the motor was cut and a red and white speedboat glided up beside the fishing-craft. And guess who was at the wheel, she told herself incredulously.

'Craig!' She ran to the rail to meet his glinting gaze. 'I thought your boat wasn't ready to take out today.

How did you——'

'Just gave the repair man the hurry-up!' He grinned up at her from the rocking boat. 'What's the problem anyway?'

'I've been waiting for ever,' she called down to him. 'Well, it seems like for ever. The other seaman hasn't turned up and we can't set sail.'

'That's what you think!' He looked inordinately pleased with himself, she thought. 'Relax! You've got yourself a skipper!'

She couldn't believe her ears. 'You mean—you'll really take me out to the island?'

'That's what I'm here for.'

Still she couldn't credit his change of mind. 'Right now?'

'We're on our way! That is,' all at once the gaiety died out of his tone and she caught an odd unreadable expression in his eyes, 'if that's what you want.'

'*What I want!*' Frustration and hopelessness gave way to the excitement of earlier in the day and her spirits soared. After the waiting she had endured today she would endure anything, anything, even if it meant accepting the offer of a man who regarded her as more or less a nuisance around his property—and showed it.

'You don't need to ask!' Delight shone in her face.

'Come on then, jump!' His arms were extended towards her. 'Don't worry, I'll catch you!'

For a moment she hesitated, turning towards the seaman at her side. 'You won't mind if I cancel the trip with you?'

He grinned encouragingly. 'You go along with your friend, you'll get there much quicker with him.'

'Just what I was thinking.' She tossed him a smile, then dropped down from the weathered timbers to find herself clasped in Craig's strong grip. Muscles rippling in his shoulders he caught her as lightly as though she were a child. Her hands were placed on his shoulders and she was piercingly aware of his nearness. All at once the world around her was a-glitter with sun and sparkle and sheer happiness. His touch was electric and as he slid her gently down to the rocking craft below, the disturbance of his hands on her waist sent her senses spinning in wild confusion. Wildly she struggled against the force of his male attraction which she seemed powerless to resist. 'How did you know,' she said breathlessly, 'that I'd be still here?'

He grinned. 'Just lucky. Are you OK?'

She answered with a brilliant smile.

'Here we go then!' He turned the key of the ignition and the engine roared into life, water churning around the blades. Then he swung the boat around, opened the throttle and sent the craft hurtling over the water.

She seated herself facing the open sea and the next moment a wave washed over the rail, drenching them both with flying spray. Craig swivelled around from the wheel, pushing the wet, dark hair from his eyes, and they laughed together. Somehow today she was finding it easy to endure his company, and she put it down to a sense of gratitude towards him for the boat trip. Anyway, why was she thinking about him? She would do better to concentrate on her own appearance. Her lips quirked at the realisation that she wouldn't present a very attractive appearance to Rick, not with her hair blown into a tangle of curls by the salty wind and the turquoise shirt clinging damply to her slim figure. But in these high temperatures her shirt would soon be dry, and anyway, she comforted herself, nothing really mattered today but she and Rick being together again.

Time slipped by in this world where there seemed

to be nothing but the throb of the engine, the dancing waves and hot sunshine. Two hours had passed when suddenly Craig turned towards her. 'See the cluster of islands ahead?' She had already caught sight of small islands covered in coconut palms that seemed to float like mirages on the calm sea.

Excitement rose in her. 'Are we nearly there?' she shouted back to him.

'The last one in the group is where we're headed!' She caught his words above the noise of the engine.

'Great!' She came to stand at his side.

Presently he cut the engine and nosed the boat towards a curve of white sandy beach. Joanne strained her eyes but she could discern no sign of habitation, nothing but the crescent of sand and beyond a hill covered in bush and palm trees. Soon they were skimming through the waves as they headed towards the shore and she could see through the translucent depths down to the sea bottom metres below.

In the shallows of the sheltered bay Joanne could scarcely contain her excitement as she kicked off her sneakers and rolled her pedalpushers up to her knees. Craig pulled the boat up on the sand and she waded ashore at his side.

Eagerly her eyes scanned the empty scene. 'There's no sign of anyone living around here.'

His tone was reassuring. 'That's because the residents live on the other side of the island near a sheltered lagoon.'

'There's no sign of Rick's boat,' her eyes scanned the empty shoreline, 'only that island outrigger canoe—wait a minute,' her voice rose on a note of excitement, 'over there under the bushes! It could be——'

Together they moved over the sand towards the

craft all but hidden in thickly growing bushes overhanging the bank.

Joanne was the first to reach the craft, turning a glowing face towards him. 'It is! It is! The *Joanne*. I knew I was right in coming here,' she cried exultantly. 'I just knew! I know now that Rick won't be far away.'

'Probably on the other side of the island.' His tone was almost uninterested. 'I'll show you the way. There's a path not far away that runs right up the hill.'

Soon they were making their way along a narrow dusty pathway that twisted and turned amongst thickly growing coconut palms. To Joanne hurrying ahead it seemed an age before they reached the top of the rise to look down on a lagoon, jewel-blue amid verdant tropical growth dotted with a few thatched huts.

'Look!' Suddenly Joanne's voice was threaded with excitement. 'That man down there fishing out by the reef. It's Rick!'

He gazed down at the tall, thin, bearded fisherman below. 'Like me to go with you?' She was too elated to notice the coolness of his tone.

'No, no, I'll be fine!' Her laughter rang out, sweet and clear on the still air. 'I just can't believe it's all happening! My lucky day!'

'You reckon?'

His flat, emotionless tone chilled her and she flung around angrily to meet his cool stare. Her lips tightened. Trust him to try to ruin the happiest day of her life! He just couldn't bear to see her happily reunited with Rick, not after his off-putting predictions regarding the chances of their meeting. What fun it would be to come running back down the hill with Rick's hand clasped in hers. A triumph over Craig—at last!

Without a word, she didn't trust herself to speak to

him right now, she turned away and began to hurry down the slope. She had gone only a short distance, however, when a thought struck her and she paused to throw over her shoulder, 'Don't wait for me! I might be quite a while. You go back to the boat.' Carried away on a high tide of elation, she could even overlook her anger with Craig. Craig with his grim, unsmiling lips and cold, pale eyes. 'I'll tell you something,' she called back to him, 'I might not be back at all tonight. I'll let you know!'

'I'll wait on the beach.' His formidable tones reached her as she sped on down the bush-lined track.

Soon she was half-way down the slope, running, her excited tones echoing on the still air. 'Rick! Rick! It's me!'

He must have heard her call, for now he was wading through the shallows. He had reached the shore when she came flying headlong down the last few yards of the track to throw herself into his arms. 'It's been so long——' She was laughing and crying all at once, gazing mistily up into his bearded face.

'That's right,' he muttered, 'a heck of a long time.'

Something was wrong, it was evident in his evasive tone and sombre expression. There was a sick feeling in her midriff and she loosened herself from his embrace. He looked oddly ill at ease, he hadn't even kissed her. Maybe, though, he had been taken by surprise. Anyway, whatever the reason for his unease, it could surely be put right now that they were together. She smiled gaily up into his eyes. 'Glad to see me?'

'Of course.' But the words had a forced inflection. 'What do *you* think?'

'I don't know. I just—wondered.' She tried for lightness. 'You look thinner than when you went away, different somehow.'

'I am different. I——' He seemed about to say more, then he changed his mind. Still, she struggled on.

'I've been looking everywhere for you. You know? On the island. I kept our date but you didn't turn up to meet me. I thought you'd been delayed, something was wrong with the boat maybe. So I just hung on here and waited for you to show up.'

He made no answer and for something to say she asked, 'There's nothing wrong with the boat, is there?'

He shook his head. 'Not now. I had a broken mast so I decided to pull in here and get some funds together. I'm still trying.'

'I know! I know!' There must surely be some simple explanation for his odd attitude towards her. 'I remembered just last night your telling me about the pink pearls on one of the islands. Are you diving for them?'

'When I can find them.' Suddenly the strained, unfamiliar tone of his voice gave way to sharp enquiry. 'Didn't you get my letter telling you——'

She pulled a face at him. 'What letter?'

He avoided her gaze. 'The one altering the arrangements about our meeting up at Rarotonga,' he said very low.

'Not a word.' But a shaft of alarm pierced her. There was something about the sombre tone of his voice, his anything but happy expression. It was almost as though he were hiding something from her, something she should have known.

'I haven't had a letter from you for eight months.' Once again she forced her voice to a light note. 'How about you? Didn't you get any mail from me? You must have picked up a few letters on your travels!'

'Only a couple soon after you took off.'

She knew now there had been a dreadful misunderstanding between them.

'Rick, what's happened in all this time we haven't seen each other that I should know about?' She held her breath for the answer.

'I'm sorry, Jo,' he said brokenly, 'terribly sorry.' He caught her to him and looking up she was devastated to see the naked pain in his eyes. Or could it be guilt? Remorse?

Don't say anything stupid. Don't let him know the feeling of utter desolation that was sweeping over her.

She dropped her gaze from his face. 'It's OK.' She heard her voice lurch. Damn! Why couldn't she handle this better? Make her voice sound firm, calm, uncaring? 'There's someone else, isn't there? A girl who's here on this island with you?'

He said with an effort, 'Mary. She and I——' She had to strain to catch the low, muttered words. 'We met up in Fiji, she was crewing on another boat in the yacht race; now she crews for me. She happens to be a diver, one of the best. She's my wife, Jo, she's good at that too!' His words died away into a silence heavy with meaning.

Shock and humiliation hit her like a physical blow. 'Makes you happy, does she?'

He said quietly, 'She's all I want, all I ever want in a woman.'

Rick, who had told her he loved her! She tried to control the trembling of her lips. Don't let him know how much it hurts.

'I guess,' she swallowed the lump that had somehow lodged itself in her throat, 'it's your life. Seems funny, though, telling me this after all the time we've known each other——' Her voice cracked and tears welled up behind her eyelids.

'Don't cry, Jo, I can't bear to see you cry. One of

these days you'll thank me for setting you free. You'll
find someone you're really crazy about, someone you'd
give up the world for.'

She brushed the moisture from her eyes with the
back of her hands, the indignant words falling from her
lips. 'But *we* were like that.'

'Never! Oh, we jogged along together well enough.
We were good mates and, sure, we got along fine. No
peaks, no valleys. Even when it came to making our
relationship a permanent one you wanted to put it off
for years while you found something more interesting
to do than sharing my life. I'll tell you something,' she
scarcely recognised this different Rick, 'we never knew
what love was, you and I!'

She eyed him angrily. 'Why do you say that? Just
because with us it wasn't fire and passion and all that
stuff? That isn't what love is all about!'

'Isn't it?' His harsh tone flayed her. 'You should
hand me a big "thank you" for setting you free to find
out for yourself. Sorry, Jo,' his voice broke, 'but you
may as well have it straight. I tried to tell you in the
letter I wrote you, it was easier that way. I'm no good at
putting things down on paper, but what we had
together was light-years away from the way a man and
woman feel about each other when it's the real thing.

'Mary, she's an Australian girl, her family and
friends are all over there but she'd leave this idyllic
existence to come with me and live on the boat or
anywhere in the world if I asked her. I wouldn't. I'm
more than happy to stay on in these islands with her.
That's the way it goes when you're *really* in love with
someone.'

A knife twisted in her heart.

'Ask yourself. All those years together and it didn't
mean a thing more than a good friendship. Oh, fine, we

had a lot going for us, but take it from me, we didn't have the one thing that mattered.'

Tears glittering in her eyes, Joanne turned on him angrily. 'If you're getting back at me for not going on that Pacific island cruise with you, for wanting to do something that happened to be important to *me*——'

He sighed exasperatedly. 'You still don't see what I'm trying to tell you, do you? If you'd really cared——'

'If *you* had.' Suddenly a feeling of desolation swept her. 'Look, this is getting us nowhere.' It was difficult but she managed to smile. Luckily he need not know that her knees were wobbly and that it was only by an effort of will that she held back the tears. 'Now I know the way things are, I'd better be getting back.'

His eyes held a puzzled expression. 'How did you get here? Did someone drop you off from a boat?'

She nodded. 'A friend.' *Friend?* She stumbled on, trying to make her voice sound carefree. 'He's waiting for me down on the beach over the hill.'

He gave a sigh of relief. 'Good.' Was he fearful that he might be stuck with her unwelcome company for the remainder of the day? Maybe even having to take her to his home and put her up for the night? For once, just for once, she was grateful to Craig for his overbearing tactics.

'It's goodbye, then.' The words seem to stick in her throat. 'Good luck!'

'Bye, Jo.' His lips brushed her cheek. 'I'll see you down to the boat if you like.'

'It doesn't matter.'

Abruptly she turned and hurried over the sand. At the foot of the bushy hill she paused to glance back but Rick wasn't even looking at her, his attention centred on a girl who was moving towards him. A small, slim girl, dark-haired. The hurtful thought came unbidden that at this distance Rick's wife could almost have been mistaken for her.

How could a man who had told her he loved her be so happy with someone else? And he still held it against her for not accompanying him on his yachting trip. But he wouldn't give up his trip for me. Or even agree to postpone it, she argued fiercely.

Vaguely amid the confusion of her thoughts she realised that the track had petered out among the palm trees, but what did it matter? She had only to go down the slope to find her way down to the beach—and Craig.

Craig! A sick feeling of humiliation surged over her. If only he didn't have to know of her disillusionment. How triumphant he would be at having been proved right about her, about Rick, about everything, damn him!

It was then that the tears came, wrenching sobs that sent the tears pouring unchecked down her cheeks. Eyes blinded with moisture, she hurried on down the hill, making her way between tall palms careless of thorny branches that tore at her flesh. Once she tripped over a pile of coconuts hidden in the long grass but she picked herself up and blundered on, leaves entangled in her hair and her face streaked with tears and dust.

When she found herself in sight of the sandy bay she half ran, half slid down the steep bank and would have fallen headlong at the foot of the slippery slope had not strong masculine hands broken her rapid descent. The next minute Craig was lifting her down to the sand. Vaguely she realised he didn't seem at all surprised at her dishevelled appearance, merely plucking a leafy twig from her hair and remarking casually, 'You missed the track by the look of things.'

'Yes, I know. I——' To her horror her voice was

drowned in a choking sob and she seemed unable to control the flow that came from a well of pain deep inside her.

'Here, take this.' He was holding towards her a snowy handkerchief he had taken from the pocket of his T-shirt. 'Now blow,' he told her as though she were a child, 'and you'll feel better.' Something about her stony face and dazed expression must have got through to him, for there was a soft light in his eyes she had never seen there before. 'Take it easy.' His tone was oddly gentle but she was too distraught to notice.

Her eyes had a blank, unseeing look, and vaguely she was aware of a trembling in her limbs. Cold chills were chasing through her and the scene around her seemed strangely unreal.

'Come on, Joanne.' His voice reached her as though from somewhere far away, as, throwing an arm around her waist, he guided her to a grassy spot in the shade of a spreading flame tree on the edge of the sand. He dropped down beside her. 'I gather,' the old ironical note was back in his tones, 'that you found your Rick.'

'Oh, yes.' She raised a stricken face. Even the vivid blue of her eyes seemed to have faded. 'It's all over,' she whispered, 'it was all a mistake. He'd found—someone else. He wrote to me about it ages ago but I,' she plucked nervously at the coarse green grass, 'didn't get the letter.'

'Tough luck.'

'And what do you know,' her voice wobbled and she heard herself running wildly on, 'Mary, this other girl, she looks a lot like me. Don't they say,' some other part of her mind seemed to be speaking without volition, 'that when it comes to love affairs a man tends to stick to a type? Just like Rick.'

He made no comment and she said very low, 'He

told me they're married, he—and Mary.' Her voice lurched and she hated herself for it. 'It was as I thought,' she stumbled on. 'He'd broken the mast of his boat, and diving for pearls on this island is the answer to his financial problems. He found out all about it on his first trip to Rarotonga. Mary, she—she's a diver too.'

All at once shock and a deep humiliation gave way to anger. 'Go on, say it!' she flung at him with trembling lips, 'I told you so, Joanne!'

His silence lent fuel to her wrath. 'You *knew,*' she accused him, staring at him from drowned blue eyes, 'all the time you knew about Rick being here on this island with another girl. You deliberately brought me here. I guess you got ever so much satisfaction from making me face up to the way things really were between Rick and me.'

'Rubbish!' His eyes were cold steel. 'Believe me, I had my suspicions of what had happened, but only because of the odd rumours that were flying around the island, talk of a guy on a boat who was living on one of the outlying islands with a girl who's a well-known yachtswoman in Australia. That was all, nothing definite.'

Reluctantly she accepted his statement. She said in a choked voice, 'Even if you had only a suspicion of the truth you could have warned me.'

'I did warn you,' ice dripped in his tone, 'and you wouldn't believe me, remember?'

She said despairingly, 'I believe you now. And the awful part of it all is,' nervously she plucked at the grass, 'he's so happy with her!' The moment the words had left her lips she would have given anything to recall them. Knowing Craig, her admission of defeat was an opportunity he wouldn't be likely to miss.

Strangely enough, however, he merely remarked off-handedly, 'Don't take it too much to heart. You'll get over it.'

She compressed her lips. Heartless brute. But a little colour had come into her pale cheeks and she felt more in control of herself.

She realised he was regarding her with his impassive gaze. 'It's home, then?'

'Oh yes, *yes!* Right away!' She got to her feet and once again the words came unthinkingly. 'Sounds funny, "home".'

He said with his quirky smile, 'You could do worse.'

Probably his way of trying to cheer me up, she thought bleakly. She lifted her shoulders and tried to steady her trembling lips. The last thing he would appreciate was a weepy female on his hands all the way back to the big island of Rarotonga.

CHAPTER EIGHT

SOON she was wading through the shallows, her eyes misted with unshed tears, as Craig guided the craft into deeper water. He helped her into the gently rocking boat and she seated herself as far away from him as possible, her tear-blotched face turned towards the sea. Almost at once, however, she found him at her side. 'Here, put this on.' He was throwing around her shoulders a man's padded windbreaker jacket.

Trust him to notice the chills that racked her slim body despite the heat of the sun's rays. All the same, she was glad of the comforting warmth and sent him a tremulous smile.

He said nothing, but grinned companionably and for a moment her heavy thoughts lifted. But almost at once the anguish was back with her, blotting out every other emotion, leaving only the pain and bleak sense of humiliation.

He started the engine and as it spluttered to life she was thankful all over again for the sudden roar that drowned out any attempts at conversation. Thankful too that Craig, his back turned towards her as he stood at the wheel, would be unaware of the fugitive tears that were stealing down her cheeks.

Back in her unit that evening the violent sobs that had racked her throughout the day were spent, leaving her drained of all feeling. With her pallid face and pink, puffy eyelids, she had little interest in her appearance, but the cotton *pareu* that left her shoulders bare was the

143

coolest and most comfortable garment she owned. It wasn't, she thought bleakly, as if she'd be seeing anyone tonight.

She wouldn't be seeing Rick again, ever. Get hold of yourself, girl, she scolded herself. Keep yourself occupied. There was one important task that must be attended to now that there was nothing to keep her here. She unzipped her travel-bag and, taking shirts and shorts from a drawer, stowed them away in the bag.

A little later a sound of knocking broke across her heavy thoughts and she went barefooted to open the door.

'Oh!' She raised lacklustre eyes to Craig's face. 'It's you!'

'Who did you expect?' She realised his discerning gaze was taking in her travel-bag lying open on the timber stand, a toilet-bag and cosmetics stowed away among clothing and sneakers.

He stood leaning against the door-jamb, thumbs hooked in the low-slung belt of his denim jeans. He appeared to be perfectly relaxed, so why did she get an impression of barely contained anger?

'Not moving out, are you?' His lazy, imperturbable tone was loaded with a meaning she couldn't interpret.

'That's right.' All at once she sensed about him an aura of authority that destroyed her defences. She heard herself nattering wildly on, her eyes fixed on the long lei of pearly pink blossoms trailing from her arms and filling the air with their sweet fragrance. 'I've been keeping this frangipani lei in the steamy bathroom for ages. I just hate to throw it out. It's still fresh after all these days.'

He ignored the remark. 'And just where,' his tone was steel, 'do you think you're off to?'

'Why,' she stared up into his closed face in surprise, 'can't you guess? Back home to New Zealand of course. There's nothing to keep me here now that——' To her chagrin her voice broke and swiftly she ran on to hide the moment of weakness. 'I'll book a seat on the plane in the morning.'

'You'll what?' The way he was looking at her, scowling and downright angry, was intimidating but she pretended not to notice. She forced her voice to a nonchalant note. 'Any objections? What's wrong with that?'

'What's wrong with it?' He stepped into the room, his expression dark and forbidding. 'Haven't you forgotten something?'

'Forgotten?' She turned away from the angry flame in his eyes.

'You have a contract with me to manage my restaurant, remember?'

'Oh, that.' She tried for lightness. 'I thought you'd understand now that—that things are different——'

'Understand what?' Anger crackled in his voice. 'You agreed to work for me on a trial basis for three months with the option of your staying on if I consider your work to be up to standard. We both thought the agreement was satisfactory, remember?' His hand shot forward to grip her shoulder in a biting clasp. 'You appear to have conveniently shelved that little matter.'

The devil! Oh, she might have known she could expect no mercy from him! 'Let me go!' she said very low. 'You're hurting me!'

His painful clasp fell away but his ice-cold tones continued to flay her. 'What do you care that I cancelled arrangements with a first-class chef that I had lined up to fly out here for the opening? Oh, I managed to fix things financially to compensate him, but no amount of cash will make up to him for the loss of working in

this particular restaurant. Luckily he's landed another
job in the same line.'

'If he's so happy in New Zealand,' she couldn't
resist the jibe, 'how come he was going to give it up to
come away over here to this tiny island?'

He said quietly, 'He was a mate of mine, a guy I'd
known for years. He knew I was making a start on a
new venture and he wanted to give me a hand to get it
off the ground. You wouldn't understand.'

'Trust men to stick together.' Her voice was brittle.

'You'd best think again,' he warned, 'before you let
me down at the last minute.'

'It's not the last minute.'

'It is, you know! I've just had a ring from my friend
and she's arriving here earlier than expected,
tomorrow, actually. Things have worked out well and
I can make the opening date a lot sooner than I
thought. I'm holding you to that contract and there's
nothing you can do about it! That is if you've got an
ounce of integrity!'

She threw him a suspicious glance. 'If you're
getting at me because of what happened about
Rick——' All at once anger mushroomed up inside her
like a cloud, against Rick, against fate and most of all
against Craig whom she hated, *hated!* 'Why don't you
come right out with it, 'she burst out, 'admit that the
reason you didn't let on to me about Rick's
whereabouts was that my being here happened to suit
your plans? It's true, isn't it?' she flung at him. 'You
wanted me to stay on the island and do your stupid
cooking! Well, I'll tell you something.' Bright flags of
danger burned in her cheeks. 'You've made a big
mistake. The last thing I'll do is work in your
restaurant. I'm off!' She tossed her head in a gesture
of defiance. 'And you can get someone else to think up

your special island menus!'

'OK,' he gritted. There was a white tinge around his mouth. 'If that's what you want to think. But don't forget,' the quietness of his tone chilled her, 'this happens to be a business deal. Pack up, cut your losses and leave the island by the first plane. That's your idea, isn't it?' His harsh tone lashed her. 'Well, it won't wash, not with me. I'm not Rick, so don't bother with the lies and excuses! I know your type, the sort that will get their own way at all costs. But not this time. Not with me!'

She said very low, 'I would have stayed if Rick——'

He waved the words away. 'Don't give me that! If you're looking for sympathy you'll have to find some other poor guy you can charm into getting your own way. You let Rick down badly. You were too bent on being a do-gooder on the other side of the world to care what was happening to him or how he felt about the situation. Don't try to tell me differently,' he went on as she tried to break into the flow of accusing words, 'it sticks out a mile.'

She glared fiercely at him. 'It wasn't like that!'

'Wasn't it?' His sarcastic tones stung her. 'Oh, it was fine to go off for a couple of years doing what you wanted to do. Fine for you. Not so good for Rick, but what did you care about him? Good old Rick, he'd wait and make the best of going on his cruise without you. He'd always done what you wanted him to do and to hell with his own wishes. You could have set him free to love someone else, a girl who was worth while, but no. Let me tell you something, a man doesn't wait for ever for a girl who says she loves him then goes haring off to leave him on his own for two years.'

Her eyes with their swollen lids were shooting danger signals. 'You know nothing about Rick and me.'

'I know you've got a contract to work for me. If you don't like it it's too bad.'

She faced him challengingly. 'I won't stay here! I won't!'

'Right. I'll ring my lawyer in the morning. I'm warning you you'll need a hell of a lot of finance to get out of that contract with me.'

'I haven't any finance,' her eyes widened in distress and anger, 'and you know it!' All at once there shot into her distraught mind a way out of the trap that was fast closing around her. 'Anyway,' she cried triumphantly, 'it wasn't a legal contract. I never did sign it and neither did you!'

'What of it? There are other ways of sealing an agreement.' Suddenly there was a dangerous quietness in his voice, 'If you'd prefer it we'll clinch the deal another way.' Her heart was pounding as he strode purposefully towards her. '*My way!*' A lambent flame flickered in his eyes. The next moment he clasped her in his arms and his lips came down on hers with savage pressure. She was helpless, pinned so close to his chest that she could scarcely breathe. His arms like steel bands around her resisted all her efforts to struggle free. Time stood still and there was nothing in all the world but his punishing kiss. At last he released her and dazed and trembling at the suddenness of her release she stumbled and all but fell.

Too shaken to speak, a hand flung to her bruised lips, she faced him accusingly.

'Agreed—partner?' His eyes seemed to be burning into hers but his tone was as cool as ever.

She found her voice at last. 'You have no right—you can't make me stay here——' She despised herself for the wobble in her voice. At that moment the ring of the telephone shrilled through the room and, scarcely aware of her movements, she lifted the receiver. A pleasant Rarotongan voice asked politely, 'Please, is Craig there?' Wordlessly she extended the receiver towards him.

Over the tumult of her thoughts she realised vaguely that it was a lengthy conversation. She would leave here tomorrow, of course she would. Yet deep down something was stopping her and she knew only too well the reason for her indecision. An ingrained honesty, 'integrity' he'd called it, was betraying her, as had happened so often in the past, reminding her of something that she had known all along. Come, now, you did promise him you'd give the job a trial run. By rushing away now you're letting him down, putting him in a spot. Maybe, just maybe, the tiny voice of truth whispered in her mind, there was a grain of truth in what he had told her. He had tried to warn her about the chances of Rick having fallen in love with another girl. He had helped her out of a desperate situation by offering her the restaurant work, even though at certain inconvenience to his own plans. If only he hadn't made her feel so furious with him——

His words on the telephone jerked her to awareness of the present, underlining her turbulent thoghts. 'The restaurant chef? No, I've got no one lined up for the job at the moment. Let me know if you hear of anyone suitable. Bye.' He replaced the receiver of the instrument in its cradle.

All at once she made up her mind. 'You've got *me!*' Could that be her own voice, not hopeless and quiet any longer but quick, bright, confident.

'You!' A light seemed to flicker in the depths of his pale eyes.

'That's right! I've changed my mind,' she said airily. Don't let him know that it mattered a lot more to her than she cared to admit that he change the rock-bottom opinion he held of her, mistaken though it was. 'Blame it on not telling a lie, keeping your word, all that stuff.'

'Great!' It was amazing how a small matter such as keeping her word to a man, a man she couldn't bear the sight of, could give her this vast sense of relief, as though a great burden had been lifted from her shoulders.

Having gained his objective, she thought huffily, he was back to his usual ways, cold, hard, unfeeling.

'Right! That's settled, then.' His formidable tones broke across her tremulous thoughts. 'Tomorrow I'll get in the rest of the food supplies for the restaurant and you can start sorting things out, making out menus for the week. There'll be a heck of a lot to get through in time for the opening.'

He turned away, pausing in the doorway to toss her his heart-knocking grin. 'I knew you'd see things my way. All you needed was a little persuasion.'

'Persuasion!' She glared balefully at his mocking dark face. 'That had nothing to do with it,' she said tersely. 'As you said, I promised——'

'So you did! How could I have forgotten!' There was a dancing glint in his eyes as he closed the door behind him.

CHAPTER NINE

ENDLESSLY through the long night Joanne tossed and turned. How could you do this to me, Rick? How could you?

And to think that Craig had been right there to witness her humiliation. Craig, of all men! She writhed at the thought. Rick's disclosure had been hard to bear, but deep down where it counted she knew that what really hurt was Craig's opinion of her. It mattered more than she would have believed possible. Now more than ever he would write her off in his book as a naïve girl who well deserved the let-down she had suffered at the hands of a man whom despite all evidence to the contrary she had blindly and stubbornly regarded as her forever devoted fiancé.

All at once she came face to face with a staggering thought. Rick and I, we've been apart for too long. We're no longer the same people as when we said goodbye two years ago. Come on now, honestly, do you really want him back? The answer came unbidden. Only because that way I would escape this awful feeling of being let down in Craig's estimation. Stupid! Stupid! She loathed the man. So why did she care so much for his opinion of her? Because he delights in triumphing over me, that's why! Because ever since I came to this island fate has conspired in one way or another to make me dependent on him.

She roused herself to sudden determination, her soft lips tightening in the darkness. But she wasn't beaten yet! She'd show him she wasn't the easily-taken-in girl he considered her. Prove to him that she was skilled, competent, trustworthy, the ideal person for the job he had offered her, albeit reluctantly. What was more, she would begin her duties right now, this minute! A few hours previously she had been furious with him for holding her to their verbal agreement. Now she couldn't wait to show him the sort of girl she really was.

Springing out of bed, she went to the windows and pulled aside the curtains. Outside there was only the intense velvety darkness of the island night. No sign of daybreak yet, and that suited her just fine. She'd make an early start on the stacked cartons of foodstuffs waiting to be sorted and packed away in cupboards and shelves in the capacious, well appointed kitchen.

Swiftly she took undergarments from the travel-bag lying open on the bench and tied around her slim waist the soft cotton garment with its pattern of shells and butterflies that was so suited to the hot climate of the islands.

Absently she ran a comb through the wayward dark curls, still damp from the shower that had washed away the dirt and sand and clinging twigs that were the result of her wild scramble through the bushes earlier in the day. In spite of herself her bottom lip quivered, but swiftly she pulled her thoughts together. Don't think of what happened at the pearl island. *Get busy.* Anything was preferable to lying in bed thinking, remembering. As she tied her hair back from her face with a ribbon a careless glance in the mirror made her pause. Could that be herself, that girl who looked utterly spent? But no matter. There would be no one to see her in the restaurant kitchen. Thank heaven for that! For the pallor of her face and her pink, swollen eyelids were a dead giveaway.

Soon she had opened the door and was out in the perfumed darkness, running across the strip of lawn, the grass cool to the touch of her bare feet.

The door of the long, low building was unlocked, as was the custom in this friendly island where folk trusted one another. She groped for the light switch, found it, and the high-ceilinged room was flooded with light. The workmen had finished painting, and under high rafters the cream-coloured walls looked light and airy. Long, gleaming benches of stainless steel winked in the light, electric ranges and microwave ovens stood against a wall, and dishwashers were fitted beneath long counters. She set the electric fans whirling and looked around her. Everything in the modern workplace was hygienic, labour-saving—and unfamiliar to her. But not for long.

She began unpacking the frozen seafoods temporarily stowed in freezers. Soon she was sorting through the various cartons of tuna, crab, prawns, oysters, stowing them away in separate sections of the huge deep-freeze cabinets.

Long before she had completed the task her hands were ice-cold and she made a mental note to get herself rubber gloves the next time she was in town.

Her hands were still numb some time later as she knelt on the tiled floor to sort out cooking ingredients and basic foodstuffs. Milk was in cartons; she had noticed an absence of dairy cows on the island. Great woven flax baskets were filled to overflowing with sugar, flour, arrowroot, tea, coffee and an assortment of spices grown on the island.

She sorted and stacked away the various items, working with care and precision, for she couldn't afford not to have cooking ingredients at hand when she needed them. Working here helped, she found, it really did. It was the only way she knew to hold at bay the nagging ache of loss and heartache. *Concentrate on the job in hand.* She clamped firmly down on the errant thoughts that surfaced in spite of her efforts to banish them. Above all, don't think of Craig. For sure, he won't be thinking of you!

The sky was lightening in the east when the noise of a car engine disturbed the silence. The next minute she realised a vehicle was pulling up at the office near by but she took little notice. The early arrival of guests from the airport was no concern of hers.

She was standing on a stepstool arranging spices on a rack above her head when the sound of voices reached her and she swung around to face Craig. At his side was a girl of twenty-six or so, tall and reed-thin. Joanne had an impression of short-cropped brown hair and eyes with an alert expression.

'Hi, Joanne!' Never had she seen Craig in this mood, his eyes alight with excitement and a note of elation tingeing his voice. 'What are you doing here at this hour of the night?'

She climbed down from the stool, words eluding her, but at last she came up with, 'It's cooler for working.'

All at once she realised he was eyeing her closely, his voice sharp and incisive. 'You look all in. Are you OK?'

'I'm fine,' she assured him, and held her breath. Had he told his companion the real reason for her wan appearance? Somehow she didn't think so. Her personal life wouldn't be all that important to him.

The next moment she realised she need not have concerned herself, his attention was completely taken up with the girl at his side. 'I want you two to get to know each other,' he was saying. 'Rob, this is Joanne, the new chef I told you about on the phone the other day.' And to Joanne, 'I told you I was going to collect Robyn from the airport tonight, remember?'

Had he told her of the other girl's arrival? She couldn't be sure. 'Hello, Robyn,' she greeted the stranger, and raised her heavy gaze to Craig's face. 'Your right-hand man, you said?' she commented, and out of the blue felt a shaft of—it couldn't be jealousy—pierce her. She rationalised away the unexpected pang. It was only because of the manner in which Craig had raved on about his super-efficient hostess-cum-travel-agent.

'Is that what he said about me?' Robyn had a clear, decisive way of speaking, Joanne thought, this girl with the thin, clever face and amused grey eyes.

She was also incredibly fresh and cool-looking, even after an all-night flight over the South Pacific ocean, Joanne mused. She wore white sandals with slender heels, her deceptively simple white linen frock crisp and uncreased, a perfect foil for the fragrant lei swinging around her tanned throat. Perfume drifted around them from tiny purple orchids, creamy frangipani blossoms and spicy white daisies gathered from gardens only hours earlier by women of the island.

Robyn was gazing speculatively around the spacious room. 'You've made a fantastic job of all this,' she said to Craig. 'Every possible labour-saving appliance with the latest in automatic ovens and oodles of working-space, lots of bench-room. Shouldn't be difficult to keep it all squeaky clean.' Her direct gaze moved to Joanne. 'Makes it easier for you when working conditions are right.' Her pleasantly pitched, self-assured tones gave evidence of a training in hostessing in the world of tourism.

Joanne nodded. 'I guess——' She broke off, having just caught sight of her reflection in a mirror hanging on the opposite wall. She had a moment's horrified picture of the sorry spectacle she presented in contrast to this poised, immaculate girl. She looked pale and drawn, dark hair curling every which way around her face. Not to mention a streak of flour across one cheek.

She was aware of Rob's clear accents. 'Looks as though we're about ready to get the show on the road!'

'We'. Why was it, Joanne wondered, that Rob's possessive tone got under her skin? And the way in which she was gazing into Craig's face. Happy . . . so utterly happy. As though Rob had found here the end of the rainbow and the pot of gold as well. Or a longed-for future with the man she loved as a working partner in their shared project on a tropical island?

It seemed to Joanne that Rob's eyes were clinging to Craig's face as though she could never look away. Clearly even although Rob had worked alongside Craig for ages, she could know nothing of the flint-hard side of his nature that he seemed to keep just for Joanne, or she wouldn't be regarding Craig in that utterly adoring way.

'You're working this girl too hard!' she told him.

Before Craig could make one of his sarcastic comments Joanne cut in quickly. 'Oh, he didn't make me. I—wanted to.'

Rob's gaze was sceptical. 'At five in the morning? And hours before that as well?'

'I didn't have to start work so early,' Joanne explained in a rush of words. 'I—didn't sleep very well last night.' If only Craig didn't volunteer the real reason for her bad night. That she couldn't endure. 'Actually,' she ran on, 'this is my first working day here. Up till now I've been just—filling in time.' *Filling in time!* 'But now that things are starting to come together and the opening day is so close,' with an effort she forced her voice to a light note, 'I thought I'd get off to an early start, you know.'

*   *   *

Hours later, Joanne was still at work in the kitchen. Nerves strung high, she went doggedly on with her tasks, knowing all too well that to allow herself to be idle would be to invite the desolate feeling of let-down, the pain and regrets.

'You're not still here!' Craig and Rob were pushing their way through the shell curtain strips in the doorway, making their way towards her. 'Come on, give it a rest,' Craig told her. 'There's no sense in knocking yourself out before you've even got the place open!'

Robyn perched on a corner of a bench, swinging long tanned legs. She had changed into a cool floral sun-frock and her smooth cap of hair was damp. Probably she had been swimming in the pool, Joanne thought enviously.

'I'm OK.' She turned her face away before Robyn could take in her work-worn, dishevelled appearance.

Craig had moved away to open the doors of deep-freezes to inspect the contents and Joanne knew a moment's satisfaction that the boss would know now that she was a worker and she meant business.

All at once she was aware of Robyn's shrewd grey eyes resting on her face. She said in her direct way, 'Craig tells me you haven't taken on the responsibility of chef for a big restaurant before. Or any restaurant, for that matter.'

'No.' Suddenly she was roused to anger. Who did she think she was, anyway? Patronising her, enquiring into Joanne's experience in the restaurant world—or lack of it! It was Craig who had put her on his payroll. So he must have some faith in her capabilities. Hurriedly she thrust away a memory of his doubtful attitude at the time he had offered her the job. She said with spirit, 'Maybe not. But I've had plenty of training.'

Robyn's thin shoulders lifted in a shrug. 'It's not the

same thing, though. Look, how about if I give you a few tips . . .?'

'It's all right,' Joanne cut in tightly.

'OK, if that's how you feel.' Anger throbbed in the low tones she was obviously doing her best to keep level. 'I'd better warn you though. Craig's a perfectionist when it comes to anything to do with this motel project. He's wrapped up in it.' She threw Joanne a meaningful glance, 'And I'll tell you something else. He hasn't much patience with amateurs.' She sent Joanne a puzzled look. 'Tell me, just how did you talk him into turning down the trained chef he had lined up to work here and giving you the job?' All at once her pleasant tones sharpened. 'Or was it just talk?' Her eyes said, it couldn't have been some wild attraction for you that made him change his mind. Even in this romantic place. Not *you*!

Joanne hesitated, furious with this interfering stranger. Confide to this contemptuous girl that Craig had taken her into his employ simply because he had taken pity on her in her desperate situation? No money, well, not sufficient for an air ticket back to New Zealand, dependent on the promise of a man she hadn't seen for two years. The thoughts ran wildly through her mind. Thank heaven Craig hadn't told Rob the facts of the job offer himself. Why should he? He just wasn't interested in her, except of course as a temporary chef for his island restaurant.

Fighting down an impulse to say 'Wouldn't you like to know?' she said with a lightness she was far from feeling, 'Oh, we just happened to run into each other.'

'How do you mean?' Robyn's voice was puzzled.

'Just down the road actually. I was on a hired push-bike and it let me down, collapsed on the road as Craig turned the corner in his car. We sort of collided. I was

knocked out for a minute. I wasn't really hurt, just
shaken, but he insisted on taking me up to the motel.
When he knew I was looking for a job in the cooking
line, maybe he felt guilty about having slammed into me
on that dangerous corner. Anyway he took me on on a
three-months' trial basis.'

Rob was eyeing her with such a look of disbelief that
Joanne ran on. 'Mind you, I happen to be able to speak
the Maori language fluently, and it's very little different
from Rarotongan, so maybe——'

'So that was it.' Rob's suspicious expression faded and
she looked more relaxed. 'Rather a lot for you to handle
though, isn't it? A brand-new venture like this. So much
depends on the quality of the restaurant meals.'

But Joanne had heard more than enough from this
patronising stranger. 'I don't think so,' she protested,
her eyes sparkling defiantly. 'The way I look at it it's a
sort of challenge, an opportunity. The start of a whole
new career for me, you know?'

Rob's expression wasn't exactly encouraging. 'I
guess,' she said doubtfully, 'that you could put it that
way.'

Joanne began picking up a pile of paper napkins
printed in motifs of native fish and butterflies, and
stacking them in a cupboard.

'I'll give you a hand with making up the menus if you
like,' Rob offered. 'You won't be used to the island-style
fruits and green vegetables and Craig wants to make a
real feature of all that. He's right, of course. Tourists
like to sample new varieties of fruits, and especially
those grown here on the island.'

As if Joanne didn't already know that. Aloud she said,
'I can manage,' and added belatedly, 'thanks all the
same.'

She squared her shoulders and there was a determined

light in her eyes. That does it! More than ever now she was determined to make a success of this job. Across the screen of her mind there flashed a picture of Rob discussing with Craig Joanne's almost certain failure to meet the high standards Craig expected of his resident chef.

But I'll make a go of it, she vowed, so help me God! She slammed the carton she was lifting on to the bench.

Robyn dropped lightly down to the floor. 'I'll leave you to it, then! Craig wants me to help him get stock sorted out for the gift shop and go over the day tours for the week, ready for all the guests arriving tomorrow. Quite exciting, isn't it, this brand-new project, something we've wanted to do for ages.' She turned away as Craig came to join her, her face lighting up as she looked at him. 'That's right, isn't it? All this, the units, the restaurant, the sports facilities and entertainments, it's been a long-time dream for you.'

He was gazing back at her, Joanne thought, as at someone in whom he had complete confidence. A trusted co-worker, a partner in his new venture, *or a woman he loved?* Now where could that absurd thought have come from, she wondered the next minute. She wrenched her mind back to his indulgent tones. 'Takes two.'

All at once he swung around towards Joanne, the pale eyes all too perceptive. 'How about you? Are you feeling OK?'

She forced a smile to stiff lips. 'Never better!' If he imagined she was going to fail him, go under completely because of yesterday's shock and let-down . . .

But her smile must have seemed genuine enough, she thought in relief, for all at once his tones were sharp and peremptory. 'You're all set for the opening tomorrow? Punchbowls with drinks prepared, glasses on hand

when the bus brings the tour crowd back from the
plane? Yoghurt and fresh fruit on serving tables as well
as cooked breakfasts? Breakfast served from seven to ten-
thirty will take care of early risers and those who went to
sleep in.'

'I know, I know.' She felt annoyed with herself at the
note of childish resentment in her tone.

'So long as you've got it all in hand.'

'Oh, I have! I have!'

For Joanne the following days went by in a haze of
activity. She spent long hours in the kitchen determined
to concentrate on nothing but the job in hand. She set
herself the task of evolving from everyday recipes
glamorous desserts incorporating the fresh mango, paw-
paw and pineapple growing luxuriously in this island
paradise. Late at night she fell into bed too weary even
for pain or regrets.

Vaguely as she passed to and from the restaurant she
was aware of the holiday atmosphere around her. Young
couples with their families splashing in the pool, men
and girls swimming amid the coral in the clear waters of
the lagoon or sipping coconut milk at the beach bar in
this world of sunshine and freedom from work and
everyday living.

From the windows of the kitchen as she worked she
caught glimpses of the minibus on its daily arrival from
the airport, the passengers wearing warm clothing they
would be glad to discard in the suddenly balmy
atmosphere.

Of Craig she had seen little, and always when she did
catch a glimpse of him he was with his 'right-hand man'.
Whether moving towards his office, entering the motel
shop or seeing guests to their units Craig and Rob would
be together. What does it matter to you that they seem to
be inseparable, she scolded herself. Nothing at all. Only

she thought Craig might have had a word with her. Two days and he hadn't even checked to see how she was getting along. He must be satisfied with the results of her labours; the special 'island' dishes she had made had eye-appeal as well as being delicious to eat. For something told her that he wouldn't be slow in letting her know had her efforts in the kitchen fallen short of his high standards in restaurant work. Not him!

Intent on her creative cuisine, she was adding the finishing touches to a halved pineapple shell filled with cubes of mango, passion fruit and bananas and laced with a liqueur.

All at once she glanced up to find Craig standing at her side. 'You're doing fine!' His glance was on the attractive dessert she was topping with a tiny island outrigger canoe with its paper sail.

'Tell me, have you got a name for this creation of yours?'

Their glances met and held, and suddenly for Joanne everything seemed to sparkle. A wild, sweet happiness was singing along her nerves. 'How about,' there was a breathless quality to her voice, 'Isa Lei, the song of the islands?'

She bent over the dish, fearful that he might read in her flushed face the wild tumult of her senses. Had he, too, felt that instant of awareness as some force flashed between them, potent and beyond their control?

His tone, however, was as controlled as ever. 'That's it! An inspiration!' She felt absurdly pleased at the warm note of appreciation in his tones.

'How about the staff you've got?' he was saying. 'Are you happy with them?'

'Oh, yes! Yes! Vera and Marie couldn't be more helpful and the boys are ever so anxious to do whatever's needed! They're all so happy and good-natured about everything, quick-thinking too. I couldn't get along without them!'

'Good for you!' Once again she was inordinately pleased by the compliment.

If only he didn't spoil it the next minute as he usually managed to do. He quirked an eyebrow towards the delectable filled pineapple dessert, and she didn't trust the glint in his eyes one little bit. 'Compliments to the local ladies and their cook book?'

'No!' She shot out the word explosively. It was an effort to force her voice to a careless inflection. 'I haven't used it yet. I haven't needed to. As I told you, I've got lots of ideas of my own!'

'Great! Anything you need here, just let me know!'

His words of appreciation must have gone to her head, she told herself, for all at once she was feeling ridiculously light-hearted.

'Just one more thing.' Bending towards her, he placed a finger beneath her rounded chin, tilting her face upwards, his probing glance taking in the look of strain and the dark shadows smudged under her eyes. His touch had started a trembling in her and she refused to meet his gaze.

'Take a break now and then,' he was saying. 'That's an order!'

'I don't know when——' At last she raised her eyes to his and scarcely knew what she was saying for the havoc he was raising with her senses.

'I'll tell you when! The barbecue by the pool. Once you've fixed all the salads and dressings, sauces and so on, the rest of the staff can put out the food on wooden platters and you can take time off and relax for a change. Take a turn at being waited on yourself. How does that strike you?'

Her stupid heart was beating a tattoo and she was

conscious only of his nearness, the crazy attraction
that drew her to him whenever he was close. She said
breathlessly, 'I really should stay on duty in the
kitchen.'

Impatiently he waved her objection aside. 'The boys
can cope with the barbecued meats, no problem. See
you by the pool at seven tomorrow night.' Suddenly
there was an intentness in his tone. 'You'll be there?'

She was trying to get the better of her runaway
emotions and she wasn't finding it easy. 'Right, boss!'
She tried to make her voice sound carefree. 'It'll be
fun to be a tourist, even if it's only for an hour or so.'

'Not tourist.' Could it be the low tone of his voice
that gave her the impression he wasn't really
interested in what he was saying? 'To the
Rarotongans anyone who comes to stay on their island
is a guest, a welcome visitor, didn't I tell you?'

She shook her head. She must have imagined the
low, emotional note in his voice a minute ago. Almost
as though her meeting him for the barbecue meal were
a matter of some importance to him. How crazy could
you get?

When he had left her she told herself she had no
intention of keeping that date by the pool. After the
feverish activity of her days in the kitchen, plus the
extra effort she put into her duties, she was fit only for
a long sleep. But deep down where it counted she
knew there was another reason, something to do with
the sight of Craig and his 'right-hand man'. For of
course he wouldn't be dining at the barbecue meal
without Rob. There was something about their close
association and happy companionship that made her
feel unaccountably angry—and oddly lonely.

Anyone would think, she chided herself, that she
was jealous of his oh-so-efficient hostess. All at once

she faced the shattering truth. She was deeply and hopelessly in love with her boss and to see him and Rob together was to invite heartache. *Real* heartache, not the mere hurt-pride variety that she had known with Rick.

She squared her shoulders and set her soft lips. But Craig wasn't ever going to suspect it. She'd die, she'd just die if he or Rob should guess her secret! Rather than hide away in her room tomorrow night she would meet the other two by the pool. What was more, she would act her part so skilfully that no one would ever know the truth.

The next day her tasks were completed earlier than she had anticipated. In her unit as she showered, the weariness of the day fell away. A smear of lilac-coloured shadow on her eyelids, a touch of mascara on her lashes was all the make-up she needed this hot night. At that moment a knock sounded on the door and she went to answer it, her feet bare on the cool tiles and the soft folds of her cotton *pareu* falling around her ankles.

'I wasn't—expecting you——'

The words came involuntarily as she found herself enmeshed in Craig's gaze. He was standing in the doorway regarding her and she wondered if she imagined tiny lights flickering deep in his eyes.

'I see you're ready for the barbecue dinner.' His cool tones wrenched her back to reality. He was freshly shaven, his dark hair damp from the shower and about him the faint tang of male cologne, and all at once she was intensely aware of him.

Wildly she struggled against his attraction. Just a physical thing, a part of the male charisma that emanated from him. What else?

Tonight, however, her senses seemed to be out of control and as he stepped towards her she had a crazy feeling he was about to kiss her. Instead he put a hand to her hair, smoothing back an unruly curl from her forehead. 'You've forgotten something. Hey, I brought you this!' Over the confusion that had taken over her senses she realised he was bending towards her, thrusting into her dark tresses a flaring pink hibiscus blossom.

Cheeks afire she snatched the flower from her hair and tossed it in the waste-paper basket.

His eyes mocked her. 'So much for love?'

'Love!' She eyed him stormily. 'I've finished with all that!'

'Are you sure?' The next moment she was enfolded in his strong arms, pressed close, close to his sinewy chest. Her pulses were racing and she was breathlessly aware of his seeking lips coming down on hers in a caress that trailed fire through her veins. Her lips clung to his in response and she wanted the moment to go on forever. The next moment he released her, and through the wild tumult of her thoughts she caught his carelessly spoken words. 'Just checking.'

She made an attempt to pull her thoughts together, knowing a moment's panic. Supposing she had betrayed her own tumultuous emotions? Wasn't it just the sort of thing he would do, trap her into betraying her feelings? She would have to prove to him that to her his kiss meant nothing. What was a kiss anyway? Don't answer that one, her heart said.

Together they strolled along the walkway in the flare-lighted darkness. At long tables by the pool Rarotongan men were barbecuing fish they had speared that morning out by the reef. There were also lamb chops, golden papaya, bananas, and for diners whose tastes ran to something more exotic Joanne had prepared baby shrimps in halved coconut shells with a cocktail sauce. Diners were seated at the small white tables grouped near the water and the sound of singing guitars fell on the night air.

As Craig saw her to her seat she couldn't help a feeling of excitement pulsing through her. Even though loving Craig was the craziest thing that had ever happened to her, even crazier than her ill-starred experience with Rick, the bittersweet happiness persisted. Just to be with him, alone together, even though she knew how little she meant in his scheme of things.

'Evening!' called a clear all-too-familiar feminine voice. As Rob came to join them at the table a little of the magic of the island night faded for Joanne. 'Sorry I'm late!' Rob was speaking to Craig as though she and he were the only ones at the table. 'I had a telephone call from New Zealand at the last minute. Tell you about it later,' she added in a low, significant tone.

Joanne told herself with a sigh that she ought not to have agreed to come here tonight. The sight of the other two with their secrets, their togetherness, hurt her afresh. Odd, because never in the past had she considered herself to be a jealous person. 'That's because you've never really loved a man before,' came the tiny voice in her mind. She thrust the painful awareness aside.

As she chatted with the other two at the table Joanne was scarcely aware of the deliciously barbecued meal. The sensation of happiness had see-sawed back and the feeling that had taken over was almost like the start of a love affair. Well, she argued away the doubts, it could be—couldn't it? Who knew? Craig's 'just checking' kiss could have been just that. And now that he knew she was free to love again . . . And despite the constant association betwen Craig and Rob, there might not really be any deep romantic attachment between them. She stole a glance towards him but his face was in shadow and gave no clue to his thoughts.

'Dance, Joanne?' She wrenched her thoughts back to
the present as he got to his feet and came towards her.
She had been only half aware of the burst of sound as
drums beat their frenzied rhythm out into the night.

She half rose from the table then dropped down again
with a laugh. 'I've broken the strap of my sandal. I'll go
back to the unit and get another pair. Won't be long!'
Kicking off the offending footwear she hurried away.

She had gone only a short distance away, however,
when she caught the sound of her own name.
Instinctively she paused. 'What about Joanne?' Craig's
usually bland tones were quick and decisive.

'Nothing! Nothing!' Rob sounded excited. 'I thought
she'd never give me a chance to talk to you in private!
Thank heaven she had trouble with her sandal. Look, I
had a ring tonight from home. I've got the most fantastic
news! It's about our wedding——'

Joanne stood transfixed in the shadows. Something
told her that it was terribly important that she should
hear what Rob was about to say.

'Oh?' Craig's tone sharpened. 'Anything important?'

'Is it ever! After all the different arrangements we've
made now it's back to square one. Mum and Dad want
us to have the wedding back there at home instead of
here on the island. Mum was quite emphatic about it.
The way she looks at it, lots of the guests wouldn't be
able to afford the air fares from New Zealand. She's got
a point there.' All at once Rob's clear accents were
threaded with uncertainty. 'You don't—mind? I mean, I
can talk Mum around to the other plan if you like?
Forget about Waipapa?'

'Not if that's the way you want it.' Joanne felt an icy
shiver creep through her. There was no doubting the
note of satisfaction in Craig's voice. 'In three months'

time we'll have the place running smoothly. I can train a manager in the meantime to fill in so that we can both get away for a few days with no worry on that score. I——'

But Joanne didn't wait to hear any more. Stunned, she turned away. Such shock waves were running through her that she scarcely knew what she was doing. Craig and Rob planning their wedding! Craig, who no doubt had found some amusement in his love-hate attitude to his resident chef. A few light kisses, a way of passing the time until Rob arrived at the island to join him. How she had misjudged him. How narrowly she had escaped falling into the trap of the masculine charisma that affected her more and more each time they met—more fool her!

Blindly she moved along the shadowed walkway, too involved in her thoughts to know or care where her bare feet were leading her. Suddenly it came to her that she had been on her way to her unit, but the purpose of her visit eluded her and anyway it didn't matter. Nothing mattered now that she knew Craig's real nature. Wait, though! Something flickered in her numbed mind. It mattered terribly that he should never know that she loved him—correction, had loved him. She faced the truth at last. She had known it all along but she had refused to allow herself to admit it.

Somehow she had to make herself join the other two and to speak and act as though there had been no shattering revelation in those overheard snatches of conversation.

Thank heaven for the dim lighting, she encouraged herself, as she neared the table by the barbecue and dropped into her seat.

'You weren't long!' Rob's voice registered disapproval. Was she wishing she had been allowed more time to discuss the wedding? Joanne wondered dully.

Craig's even tones were expressionless. 'Changed your mind about dancing tonight?'

I wish I could change my mind about caring for you! Aloud she heard herself murmuring, 'Yes, yes, I did.' She could scarcely collect her senses. 'I don't mind really,' she added lamely, 'I'm feeling a bit tired.'

She knew she wasn't handling this at all well, but a dreadful weariness of the spirit was taking over. No wonder the other two were silent. Even in the gloom she knew they must be regarding her oddly. Were they fearful that she might have overheard that very private conversation between them a few minutes ago? Somehow she would need to play her part more skilfully than this.

She would give anything to have a second chance. And isn't it just at times like this, she thought the next moment, that fate takes a hand in things?

For a masculine voice was hailing her. 'It's you!' Delight and relief rang in his tones. 'It's really you!'

A tall, lanky young man was hurrying eagerly towards her, his sandy-coloured hair catching the gleam of the flares.

'Rick!' Her cry rang out before she could stop to think.

CHAPTER TEN

THE next moment she realised her mistake.

'Remember me?' he was saying eagerly. 'The tavern in town? You took me for another guy.' There might not have been anyone else at the table for all the notice he was taking of the other two. He was bending towards her. 'You didn't ever come across him then, that yachting guy you were looking for the night we met up at the tavern?'

'Yes, no, well——' She was acutely conscious of Rob's curious stare. She couldn't bear that Rob should hear the story of the distraught girl who had been desperately searching for a man who had all but forgotten her.

Suddenly there was an urgency in the boyish tones. 'You've changed your mind about him? That's it, isn't it?'

Her voice was barely audible. 'Something like that.'

'Great!' Clearly he was elated by the words. 'That's the best news I've had in weeks, two weeks actually. Do you realise it's just that long since I caught sight of you and lost you right afterwards? We've got a lot of wasted time to make up.' For the first time he appeared to become aware of her companions at the table. He grinned companionably towards the other two. 'Don't mind me. I just can't believe my luck! I've been combing the island for this girl and now I've found her I'm not letting her out of my sight.' He seemed unable to take her eyes from her face.

'You wouldn't believe the hours I've put in looking

171

for you,' he told Joanne. 'I've haunted the bars, restaurants, taverns but there was never a sign of a girl with the most vividly blue eyes I've ever seen and soft curly black hair. And then tonight, just by chance,' his excited tones deepened, softened, 'I've found you. I've really found you—at last.'

He was younger than Rick, she realised now, young and carefree and probably in a holiday mood, and something about her had stayed with him after their brief encounter when she had for a moment mistaken him for Rick. The thoughts flew through her mind. What did it matter to her whether he was young or old, fair or dark; he was her escape route and she intended to take full advantage of the opportunity fate had handed her.

'She's going to dance with me,' he was saying on an elated note to the others. 'That's right, isn't it?' As he turned towards her she realised he didn't know her name.

She forced a smile to her lips. 'Joanne.'

'I'm Kevin. Come on.' He grasped her hand and drew her to her feet. 'Let's go!'

'Hold on.' Craig's ironic tones halted her. 'Haven't you forgotten something? Your broken sandal?'

She flashed him a defiant glance. He was taking a positive delight in needling her. Indeed, the ridiculous thought came unbidden, the way he was looking at her, if she hadn't known better she might have thought him to be jealous of the other man. And yet, why not? So strong was Craig's aura of attraction that she could almost *feel* it. Girls would find it difficult not to be drawn to him, even against their conscious will. Her lips tightened. Didn't she know it?

For once, however, the ball was in her court and she intended to take full advantage of it. She schooled her tone to a light-hearted inflection. 'I'll dance the way the Rarotongans do—barefooted. It's better that way!'

'That's the spirit!' her escort agreed with a delighted grin.

'Well!' As they moved away she caught Robyn's incredulous murmur. But what did it matter what Rob thought about her, or Craig either for that matter? There seemed to be a lump lodged in her throat and she tried to swallow it away. The other two would be only too glad to be free of her, now they could discuss their . . . wedding plans in private.

'Joanne,' her companion was saying happily, 'nice name.' She wrenched her mind back to the boyish tones. 'That couple back there? Friends of yours, are they?'

Friends! 'My boss,' she said briefly, 'and Rob, she's a sort of manageress.' Merely coupling the names brought an unexpected stab of the heart.

He said in a surprised tone. 'You work here?'

She tried to pull her thoughts together. 'I'm chef at the restaurant, on three months' trial actually.' She must have been out of her mind to tie herself down to work here for three long months. 'There are other ways of sealing an agreement.' Craig's low vibrant tones echoed in her memory and the passionate poignancy of his kiss was something she couldn't banish from her mind.

Kevin drew her to a stop in the shadows and she tried to concentrate on his young, excited tones. 'The way I figured it, you liked that other guy a lot. Maybe, I thought, with a bit of luck you wouldn't find him. I'm a good substitute, you'll see,' he said laughingly. 'You'll be glad. Funny,' he ran on, 'you mightn't believe this, but I only saw you for those few minutes but somehow I couldn't get you out of my mind. Not one of the girls I've met since then meant a thing to me, so I thought I'd better do something about it. Go looking for you. But no luck. I'd decided you must have found your yachtsman and gone back to——'

'Kiwiland, actually,' she put in. 'Only I didn't go back there.'

'Lucky for me! Then just on a chance I thought I'd have a look around here.' His voice changed to excitement and happiness. 'The best decision I ever made!'

Over the ache in her heart she was aware of his glance resting on her downcast face. His voice, eager, happy, *real*, unlike Craig's treacherous beguiling tones, rang with elation. 'I can't believe it yet! To think I've found you!'

Why did it always have to be the wrong man? Why couldn't she be happy in his company? She should be, when he reminded her so much of Rick that it was ridiculous. But Rick didn't matter to her any more, only Craig, and he . . . She thrust the thought aside. Don't think of Craig. Forget him, he's not worth thinking about. Aloud she said restlessly, 'Feel like dancing?'

'Anything, so long as I've got you with me.'

Soon they reached the spacious room where couples were taking the dance floor. The infectious beat of the drums pulsed around them and Joanne was glad of the wild exuberance of the dance. Tonight the exciting movements suited her mood, too fast for regrets or heartache. All around were young Rarotongan men and women, leis swinging from their necks and thick, shiny leaves accentuating swaying hips as they moved faster and faster to the sensuous rhythm of the wooden drums.

Gradually as the tempo increased only the natives of the country and Joanne and her partner remained on the floor. The beating drums rose on a wild crescendo and Joanne's dark curls flew around her flushed face.

She was breathless when at last a crash of sound signalled the end of the dance. Kevin too was flushed and out of breath as they moved away from the dance floor. 'How about a stroll along the beach to cool off?' he suggested.

'If you like.' She tried to summon some enthusiasm into her tones, but it was difficult.

As they threaded their way among the tables by the pool she could see Craig's dark head bent close to Rob's cropped hair and a stab of pain pierced her. No doubt they were engrossed in their own wedding plans, she thought on a sigh, for neither noticed as Joanne and Kevin went by in the gloom. What did she expect?

Down on the sands the stars hung like brilliants in the soft darkness of the night sky and the booming of the surf was loud in the stillness. An errant breeze rattled the palm fronds on the bank and stirred Joanne's tresses and cooled her hot cheeks.

She was only half aware of Kevin's enthusiastic tones. What was he saying? Something about tomorrow. They could make a day of it. Swim, snorkel, or how about a trek across the island?

She let him run on, making suitable replies, but her mind was filled with thoughts of Craig and Rob and she scarcely took in what her companion was saying.

They moved a long way, leaving the lighted complex behind them and strolling along the sand, the only lights now in sight those of fishermen in the bay. When at last they made their way back to the motel the pool tables were empty and only a few late drinkers were seated on stools at the beach bar.

It wasn't until they reached the steps leading up to her unit that she roused herself from her heavy thoughts to concentrate on Kevin's eager tones. 'You'll enjoy the run out tomorrow. I'll take a day off work.'

She roused herself to say, 'You're not here on holiday,

then?'

'No such luck! I earn a crust at the local hospital as a medical student. I'm over here on a two-year stint from New Zealand.' All at once his tones were anxious. 'You will come with me tomorrow? It's a date?' At last his words penetrated her numbed senses and she realised he was eyeing her intently. 'Please. Now that I've found you I don't want to let you go. Make it tomorrow! I'll pick you up at nine, shall I?'

'Out of the question,' cut in a cool masculine voice, and Joanne's heart gave a traitorous leap. Craig! She hadn't noticed him as he stood in the shadows of the bushes.

'You'd better put your friend in the picture, Joanne!' Craig made no apologies for his interference in her affairs and she knew only too well that his authoritative tone meant business. 'Better let him in on the fact that you happen to be a working girl and you're on duty in, let's see,' he consulted the illuminated dial of his wristwatch, 'a few hours' time.'

As Joanne took in Kevin's stricken expression she berated herself for her selfishness in not making the position clear to him earlier in the evening. Somehow it hadn't seemed important; nothing to her seemed to matter now that she had learned of Craig and Rob's wedding plans.

'That's how it is, I'm afraid,' she agreed, 'but there'll be another time.'

Eagerly Kevin clutched at the suggestion. 'You must get a free day before too long.'

Uneasily aware of Craig's sardonic face in the shadows she heard her own voice saying, 'Of course I do but not for a while. We've just had the opening of the motel. I'll let you know when I'm free.'

'I can't wait that long to hear from you! I'll keep in

touch. Ring you tomorrow. Till then.' He sent an uncertain glance towards Craig, a tall, somehow menacing figure in the shadows. 'See you, Joanne.'

'Night,' she whispered, and as he turned away she immediately forgot him.

All at once disillusionment and heartache gave way to a dark cloud of anger. 'I don't know why you had to follow me!' she accused Craig hotly.

'Follow you?' came his deceptively innocent tones. 'Why would I do that?'

'I don't know!' she flung back at him. 'But it seems like that.'

'I brought you these,' ice tinkled in his tone, 'thought you might be needing them in the morning.' He thrust her sandals into her hands and blindly through the wild emotion that was throbbing through her she could feel the broken strap was now intact.

'You've—mended them?' If only he didn't catch the betraying tremor in her voice. 'Th-thanks.'

'Nothing to it. Joanne——' The husky softness of his voice sent quivers through her, but the next minute she steeled herself not to yield to the magic of the sensuous night and the spell of his nearness. Remember, he's not for you.

'I've got to go in,' she muttered, aware that he was moving towards her. 'I'd better catch up with some sleep.' She flew up the wooden steps to pause at the top and throw back over her shoulder, 'Night!'

'Goodnight, Joanne.'

As she reached her doorway she glanced back over her shoulder but he was still standing where she had left him. Craig seemed to have got the message at last, to realise that she meant what she said. If only . . . As she let herself into her unit she wondered why her hands were trembling.

Her work garments were lying on the bed where she had tossed them. Surely it was another lifetime since she had known for a brief time what happiness could be when you were with the man you loved. But that was before she had learned that he was not to be trusted and she had best forget him.

It's your own fault, piped the tiny voice deep in her mind. Anyone but a besotted fool like her would have known the truth about Craig and Rob long ago, but she had ignored the obvious signs because she had wanted to. Hadn't he confided to her that the ring with its rare pink pearl he had bought in town was for Robyn? She had somehow managed to put the matter of the ring out of her mind. She must have been in love with him even at that time. They way in which he had raved on about the other girl should have told her that Rob meant everything to him. She knew now that she had refused to face the truth, idiot that she was. Now she must make herself forget him. With Craig as her boss? Seeing him, hearing his vibrant tones every day? It wasn't going to be easy.

'That you, Joanne?' Beside her bed the telephone shrilled and as she answered the call Kevin's enthusiastic young tones echoed in her ears. 'I'm still hoping. You must be due for that day off work soon! When am I going to see you again?' It was a question he had asked her over the phone each morning since they had met in the motel.

'Tomorrow. I've got the day free, well, most of it.'

'Terrific! I've really been looking forward to that!' Delight tinged his tones. 'Haven't you?'

'It's a break.' He wasn't to know that she was spending the hours away from her job with him only because the alternative involved either going off among strangers on the minibus to a beach picnic Rob had arranged or taking herself for a walk along the sand. Anything to escape from the sight of Craig and Rob together.

She wrenched her mind back to Kevin's voice. 'How would you feel about a tramp up the mountain?'

'Sounds great!' At least that was the truth. 'I'll bring along a picnic lunch if you tell me what you want?'

'*You!*'

She managed a light laugh. 'You scarcely know me.'

'Give me time! I'm working on it!'

'You mightn't like me if you really knew me.' What would you say if I told you that I'm hopelessly, desperately in love with a man who's going to marry another girl?

Kevin's light-hearted tones seemed to zero in on her thoughts. 'I'll risk it! How does ten o'clock suit you?'

'Just fine.'

'And don't forget your bikini, you might need it. See you!'

As she replaced the receiver her soft lips drooped. Kevin was betraying all the signs of falling in love with her despite their short acquaintance. A sigh escaped her. Why did it always have to be the wrong man?

When Kevin was to call for her she was ready for the outing early. Thank heaven she looked normal enough, she mused, as she checked her appearance in the mirror. Her buttercup-yellow halter-top with its matching shorts was fresh and bright-looking and made a suitable cover-up for the bikini she wore next to her skin.

Sunglasses were in her shoulder-bag, she had already applied sunscreen lotion to her face. Now all she had to do was to slip yellow sneakers on her feet and she would be ready, all except for her smile! She must remember to smile a lot today, to look as though she were enjoying herself.

In the small kitchen she moved to the refrigerator and took out the chicken sandwiches she had prepared the night before. She added crackers and wedges of cheese and filled a Thermos cooler with mango and passion-fruit juice, then threw into the woven basket a bag of breadfruit chips.

The next moment she opened the door to meet Kevin's happy grin.

'Hi! All set to go. Do you know something, this is the first time I've seen you in daylight.' His eyes said a lot more. 'I couldn't believe my luck,' he ran on as he took the picnic basket from her, 'when you told me you'd come out for the day with me.'

As they went down the steps together he went on, a shade of embarrassment in his tones. 'I mean, that other guy, the one you said looks like me.'

She made her voice light and careless, 'You mean, Rick?'

'That's the one.' He seemed to get the words out with difficulty. 'There's something I've got to ask you.' He swallowed, looked away. 'What I'm trying to say—my looking like him. You don't mind?'

'Good heavens, no!' It was easy to sound carefree where Rick was concerned. 'It doesn't bother me,' she assured him, 'why should it?'

'I don't know,' he said in a low tone, 'I guess I thought——'

'You thought wrong!' She softened the words with a smile. 'Now you can really enjoy the day!'

Outside a soft, warm rain was falling, misting the bushes around them and beading Joanne's hair with drops of moisture.

'Liquid sunshine, the islanders call it,' Kevin said with a grin. He went around to open the door of the car standing in the driveway then slid into the driver's seat beside her.

Soon they were taking the old coral road leading to the interior of the island where the jagged mountain peaks were lost in mist. On either side of the road Joanne could see rich tropical bush, for straggling streets with painted bungalows had given way to villages where thatched huts were all but hidden in coconut and banana plantations, chickens ran free among the trees and pigs rooted happily in unfenced gardens.

'Still feel like that hike?' he said with a grin as he drew up not far from an old crater in a mountain.

She threw him a smile. 'I belonged to a tramping club back home would you believe?' She tried to make her voice light and careless.

It wasn't long before he was pulling up the car at the foot of a high, jagged mountain peak. Soon they were taking the track winding over shifting scoria of an old crater.

At last, hot and breathless, they scrambled the last few feet to the summit. Joanne paused on the mountain top to wipe the dust and perspiration from her flushed face. 'It was worth the climb,' she told Kevin. The rain had cleared away and the spectacular view of both sides of the island was outspread far below.

A short rest, then they were making their way down the bush-covered slope. Kevin had clasped her hand in his but the physical contact meant nothing to her. She must get over this stupid infatuation for Craig, for that was all it could be, she told herself.

'Surprise, surprise!' Kevin called laughingly as they pelted down the last few feet of the incline to come in sight of a waterfall. A rainbow shimmered in the flying spray and water cascaded endlessly down from heights far above to splash in a welter of foam in the pool below.

Already Joanne was slipping off her halter-top and shorts and climbing over the rocks to drop into the sunlit pool. A few moments later Kevin joined her in the water.

After a time they dropped down on lush grass near the pool and Joanne unwrapped the sandwiches. 'Nothing glamorous, just plain fare.' She was aware of his adoring gaze fixed on her face. 'I don't think you'd notice today if I brought plain bread with me.'

'How did you guess?'

'I didn't bring any fruit,' she said later as they washed down the last of the crackers and cheese with juice.

'No need, it's instant service around here!' Springing to his feet, he plucked a ripe golden paw-paw, warmed by the sun, from a cluster of fruit hanging from a near-by tree.

'Perfect,' she murmured when he had taken a knife from his pocket and handed her the fruit.

'Everything's perfect today,' Kevin said significantly.

Swiftly she dropped her gaze, fearful he might catch the shadow of sadness in her eyes she was trying so hard to conceal.

She was kneeling on the grass packing away the remains of the picnic lunch when she felt his arms stealing around her shoulders, his face pressed close to hers. 'If you only knew. Ever since I saw you that night at the tavern I've been looking for you, hoping I'd be lucky, but I didn't even know your name and no one I asked had heard of you. At last I came to a dead end. Most folk only come to the island for a week's holiday. And then,' she could scarcely catch his low excited tone, 'to find you!' He was drawing her close, but some instinct she couldn't define made her pull herself free.

'Don't be like that,' he begged, 'just give me a chance.' Lifting her small tanned hand to his lips he covered her palm with kisses.

Trying for lightness she said, 'As I told you, we scarcely know each other.'

'Don't we? I'll soon put that right!' Before she could guess his intention he had pressed her to him, his lips coming down on hers with gentle pressure. Only for an instant, then she had drawn away.

'OK.' Hurt and bewilderment tinged his tones. 'If that's the way you want it.'

She lifted her heavy gaze to his downcast face. 'It's got nothing to do with you.'

Immediately his expression brightened. 'You mean there's a chance for me—for us to get to know each other better, a lot better?'

She shifted evasively. 'Who knows?' To change the subject she ran on quickly. 'Tell me about yourself. I suppose you really enjoy working here on the island.'

'It's great!' To her relief she realised he had recovered his good humour. 'A job I like in the hospital with a holiday atmosphere thrown in as a bonus. What do you think?' All at once his tones were tinged with regret. 'I'd like it better still if my mate were still working alongside me. He finished his stint at the hospital some months ago and went home to take up a practice there. Wayne's a terrific guy. I sure miss him a lot. He's no letter-writer though, so I never expect to get any news from him. I haven't had a word from him since he took off back to New Zealand.'

For something to say she replied, 'Maybe you'll see him in New Zealand before long. When you take a holiday back home.'

'How did you guess?' The youthful enthusiasm was back in his voice. 'I had a phone call from him last night. Big news! He and Megan have decided to get married in Waipapa, it's her home town. They had planned to have the wedding over here. He's got a brother with a motel somewhere on the island but that idea's all off now, it seems.' His lips curved reminiscently. 'I still can't believe it. Those two, Megan and Wayne, have parted and made it up so many times you wouldn't believe. This time it looks as if they're really going to tie the knot. It's hard to picture young Megan settling down as the wife of a country doctor. She works in Auckland as a travel consultant and somehow I always expected her to end up a dedicated career girl like her sister Robyn, from what Wayne tells me about her.' He broke off, eyeing her in surprise. 'Don't look so surprised! Couples do get married, even in Waipapa.'

Joanne opened her lips to speak then closed them again, the thoughts tumbling wildly through her mind. Had she jumped to the wrong conclusions regarding that scrap of overheard conversation? Could it be another couple, Rob's young sister, Craig's brother, who had been the subject of their discussion?

Kevin was still talking but Joanne was no longer listening. Her eyes were fastened intently on his face. 'Tell me, what is your friend's name?' She held her breath for the answer.

'Wayne? It's Summers. New Zealand's such a sparsely populated place, you might know the name.'

Did she know the name! She threw him a radiant look. 'Sort of.'

Her heart was beating a tattoo and her world had turned upside down to tumble back into place. It was a new and exciting world where anything could happen. Anything!

Suddenly she couldn't wait to get back to the motel, and Craig. What she had just learned concerning him and Rob forced everything else from her mind. Just to see him, to hear the vibrant tones of his voice, even if it was only nothing things he spoke of, like restaurant menus. She couldn't live without him!

'You're very quiet all of a sudden.' Kevin's friendly tones broke across her rioting thoughts. All at once there was an anxious expression in his eyes. 'Have I said something?'

She rallied herself and sent him a brilliant smile. 'It's not you. I've really enjoyed the day'—*liar*—'but I guess I've got to get back. I did say I'd be in the restaurant in time to prepare the evening meal.' She glanced down at the digital watch she had bought in the township. 'It's getting very late.'

'What of it?' Kevin's face had darkened. 'It's that boss of yours, isn't it?' His voice hardened. 'If he makes any trouble for you, just put him on to me! I wouldn't mind having a go at him. He's got it in for me. Hanging around your unit the other night, not leaving us to ourselves. I should have taken him then!'

'No, no.' Joanne was half laughing, half concerned by the threat. 'Don't do anything like that!'

'Scared of losing your job, is that it?' he shot back at her. 'He's got you just where he wants you. Funny thing,' all at once his belligerent tones changed to a puzzled note, 'I'd have sworn you'd be the last one in the world to be under the thumb of an employer, a spirited girl like you!'

'You don't understand!' she burst out. 'You've got it all wrong! Craig, well, he's simply wrapped up in this complex he's running, he insists that everyone on the payroll attends to their duties really efficiently, but he treats his staff well.'

'Spying on them after hours?' Kevin's lips curved scornfully. 'Shoving his spoke in where it's not wanted? If you ask me the guy's nuts about you and he can't stand any other man being near you. He's in love with

you! Anyone can see it! He was mad as hell with me the
other night, you could tell that by his tone of voice. He
just couldn't take the thought of another guy taking you
out for a day away from his damned hot kitchen!'

He's in love with you. She could scarcely breathe for
the sweet excitement that was sweeping through her
senses. Wildly she said, 'It's not a hot kitchen! The
fans——'

To her relief Kevin's attention was diverted. 'If you
say so,' he murmured sulkily.

The thrilling possibilities evoked by Kevin's angry
outburst stayed with her all the way to the motel. But in
her room the doubts crept back into her mind. It wasn't
true, of course, that Craig cared for her. How could it
be, when just being together sparked them into spirited
encounters? Come to think of it—she tried to wrench
her thoughts back to sanity—for one reason or another
he was mad with her most of the time.

Swiftly she changed into a cotton *pareu*, the sea-blue
shade of the island-style garment complimenting the
golden tan of her bare shoulders.

Back in the kitchen with her softly spoken, olive-
skinned workmates the hours seemed to fly by.
Everything appeared to be going along smoothly. Or
could it be merely that her own life had changed so that
no task seemed any bother to her, not with the wild
sweet knowledge she was hugging to herself?

All the time as she worked her thoughts were busy.
Suppose now that there were no misunderstandings
between her and Craig, nothing to keep them apart . . .
The idea was new and intoxicating. She loved him,
loved him. If only he felt the same way about her, this
man who never gave anything of himself away!

She found herself endlessly eyeing the doorway,
watching for his tall figure. Always when he came into

the room his glance seemed to seek her out. Was it only to satisfy himself that despite the risk he had taken in employing her, the new chef wasn't doing so badly after all?

In the end it was Rob who entered the kitchen, her shrewd gaze moving over the Rarotongan workers before she came to stand at Joanne's side. In the past, Rob's supercilious manner and silent scrutiny of the food she was preparing would have put her in a flap, but not any longer. 'Everything's fine,' she said brightly. All at once it came to her that Rob lived only for her career, and the pinpricks and criticisms so often levelled in Joanne's direction had no personal basis. Why hadn't she realised all this before?

As the hours went by and Craig did not appear Joanne's high spirits flagged. She told herself that considering her suddenly changed attitude to him on the night of the barbecue dinner she could scarcely expect him to seek her out. Kevin *must* have been mistaken in his assumption concerning the boss's feelings for her.

It was long past midnight when at last she made her way back along the shadowed walkway. The island night was bathed in silver as a full moon sailed overhead and stars hung like crystals in the soft darkness of the night sky. Faintly from the villages near by came the rhythmic beat of drums. It was a night for love. Joanne's soft lips drooped. The chances were that Craig couldn't care less about her.

All at once she caught an echo of footsteps behind her and she glanced back to see a tall masculine figure. Her heart was beating madly. Only one man she knew walked so straight and tall. She paused as Craig caught up with her.

'I thought I'd catch you,' he said evenly. 'There's something I want to ask you.'

'Oh!' The moon emerged at that moment from a bank of clouds painting planes and angles on his face. No emotion there. Her heart sank. He looked as cool and impassive as ever. She must have been crazy to have attached any special significance to his everyday words.

'Enjoy your day with your look-alike boyfriend?' There was a terse, angry edge to his voice.

As always she was piercingly aware of his nearness. Could it be her own voice sounding so normal and uncaring? 'Oh yes, it was super.'

'Another Rick to keep you happy?' She flinched at the contempt in his tone. 'You'd scarcely be aware of the difference.'

'It's not what you think!' she burst out angrily.

'He must have something,' he bit out gruffly, 'to get you falling for him so easily! Another Rick to salvage your pride, is that it? Or aren't you particular about your menfriends?' he taunted softly.

Tiny hammers of pain and anger were beating in her head and her eyes were shooting sparks. 'You're all wrong about Kevin, about everything! You know nothing about me or how I feel.' She gritted her teeth. 'As if you'd care.'

She barely caught his low tones, hoarse with emotion. 'I care.'

The timbre of his voice, potent as a caress, sent her senses spinning in wild confusion. All at once the atmosphere was tense with emotion and she knew that he was about to kiss her. A sudden dizzy happiness surged through her and she longed to touch him. Impelled by an instinct beyond her control she swayed towards him, then his mouth was seeking hers, sending fire through her pulses as her lips clung to his, powerless against the delight of his caress.

A delicious madness was taking over and she revelled in the hard man-feel of him through the thin cotton of his shirt. He was covering her face, her throat, with kisses. A dreamy rapture held her captive and when at last reality returned she drew a ragged breath. 'What was it—you wanted to see me about?'

He said huskily, 'I want you to marry me.' He raised a hand to smooth the dark curls back from her flushed face. 'I love you, my darling. You are my life.'

'I love you too.' Her eyes were sparkling like twin sapphires as she looked tremulously up at him. The words she was about to say were lost in the heady sweetness of his caress.

Much, much later she stirred in his arms. 'You know, all this time I really thought that you and Rob——'

'Rob!' His voice was incredulous.

Her fingers traced the outlines of his lean dark face. 'Seems stupid now, doesn't it, but the way I saw it you were always with her. And the night of the barbecue I happened to overhear some talk between you. It was when I broke the strap of my sandal, remember? you wree making arrangements for a wedding with her, and I took it——'

He held her at arm's length to smile down into her face.

'Rob! Good grief! We were just about brought up together, she's like a sister to me!'

'I know, I know now that it's a family affair. Kevin told me about it, although he didn't realise what it meant to me. He happens to be a friend of the bridegroom. But that night at the barbecue I got such a shock. I took it that you were getting married——'

'True.' His words were punctuated with kisses as he held her close once again. 'To the girl I love more than anything else in the world.' The urgent pressure of his lips sent tingles of excitement through her pulses. 'Let's get married right here on the island, where we belong!'

THREE UNBEATABLE NOVELS FROM
W⊕RLDWIDE

STOLEN MOMENTS by Janice Kaiser   £2.75

To escape her tragic marriage Lacey Parlett kidnaps her daughter
and is forced into hiding. Now, with the FBI closing in, she is desperate
to stay anonymous – but one man is dangerously near to discovering
her secret.

SARAH by Maura Seger   £2.95

The first of three novels in top author Maura Seger's captivating saga
on the Calvert family introduces Sarah – a formidable woman torn
between the man she loves and a society she hates during the American
Civil War.

STRONGER BY FAR by Sandra James   £2.50

Kate McAllister's ex-husband has been kidnapped. With less than 48
hours to meet the ransom demands, she has only one option left. . .
one she had sworn never to take!.

**These three new titles will be out in bookshops from
April 1989.**

*Available from Boots, Martins, John Menzies, W.H. Smith, Woolworths
and other paperback stockists.*

Mills & Boon

YOU'RE INVITED TO ACCEPT **FOUR ROMANCES** AND A TOTE BAG **FREE!**

Acceptance card

| NO STAMP NEEDED | **Post to: Reader Service, FREEPOST, P.O. Box 236, Croydon, Surrey. CR9 9EL** |

Please note readers in Southern Africa write to:
Independant Book Services P.T.Y., Postbag X3010, Randburg 2125, S. Africa

YES! Please send me 4 free Mills & Boon Romances and my free tote bag – and reserve a Reader Service Subscription for me. If I decide to subscribe I shall receive 6 new Romances every month as soon as they come off the presses for £7.50, together with a FREE monthly newsletter including information on top authors and special offers, exclusively for Reader Service subscribers. There are no postage and packing charges, and I understand I may cancel or suspend my subscription at any time. If I decide not to subscribe I shall write to you within 10 days. Even if I decide not to subscribe the 4 free novels and the tote bag are mine to keep forever. I am over 18 years of age   EP20R

NAME _____
                                              (CAPITALS PLEASE)

ADDRESS _____

_____

_____ POSTCODE _____

Mills & Boon Ltd. reserve the right to exercise discretion in granting membership. You may be mailed with other offers as a result of this application. Offer expires June 30th 1989 and is limited to one per household.
Offer applies in UK and Eire only. Overseas send for details.

HOW FAR CAN LOVE BE CHALLENGED?

REDWOOD EMPIRE *By Elizabeth Lowell* £2.95

The best-selling author of *'Tell Me No Lies'*, creates a bitter triangle of love and hate amidst the majestic wilderness of America's Northwest empire. 19-year old Maya Charter's marriage to Hale Hawthorne is jeopardized by her lingering feelings for her former lover – his son, Will.

CHERISH THIS MOMENT *By Sandra Canfield* £2.75

Senator Cole Damon is Washington's most eligible bachelor, but his attraction to journalist Tracy Kent is hampered by her shocking past. If their love is to survive, he must first overcome her fear of betrayal.

BEYOND COMPARE *By Risa Kirk* £2.50

When T.V. presenters Dinah Blake and Neil Kerrigan meet to co-host a special programme, the only thing they have in common is their growing attraction for each other. Can they settle their differences, or is their conflict a recipe for disaster?

These three new titles will be out in bookshops from March 1989.

W●RLDWIDE

Available from Boots, Martins, John Menzies, W.H. Smith, Woolworths and other paperback stockists.